Working Safely with Chemicals in the Laboratory 2nd Edition

Editor: Christine E. Gorman

Contributors: John V. Conforti
Maureen Gannon
Erik M. Roy
Marilyn J. Wurth

Technical Reviewers: Dr. Antony C. Wilbraham
Dr. Catherine Franklin

Published by:
Genium Group, Inc. (www.genium.com)
1171 RiverFront Center • Amsterdam, NY 12010 • (518) 842-4111

ISBN 0-931690-69-2
Printed in Canada

6th Printing 2005-08

***Working Safely with Chemicals in the Laboratory* is available with your institution's name imprinted on the cover.**

Contents

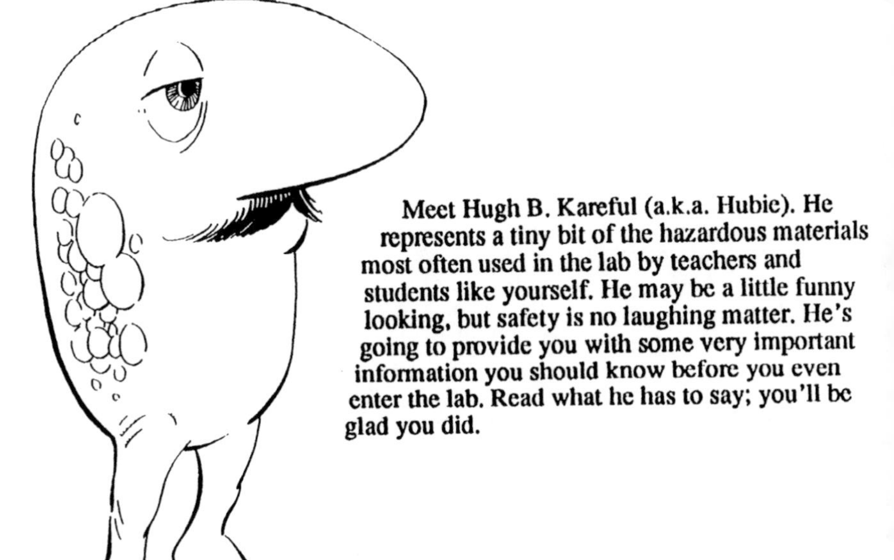

Meet Hugh B. Kareful (a.k.a. Hubie). He represents a tiny bit of the hazardous materials most often used in the lab by teachers and students like yourself. He may be a little funny looking, but safety is no laughing matter. He's going to provide you with some very important information you should know before you even enter the lab. Read what he has to say; you'll be glad you did.

EMERGENCY PHONE LOG

In case of emergency

Call ____________________

If you have a question or concern regarding your safety in the laboratory

Call ____________________

Campus Security ____________________

Campus Infirmary ____________________

Emergency Medical ____________________

Fire Department ____________________

Other Important Numbers:

____________________ ____________________

____________________ ____________________

____________________ ____________________

____________________ ____________________

Name: ____________________ **Course:** ____________________

Instructor: ____________________

I. Meet the Accused

The Feds finally caught up with me, and now I'm singin' like a canary. They promised me the easy life if I cooperate. No more cleaning up bathroom floors, or boiling over in laboratory test tubes. I've got the goods on the nastiest members of my family, and I'm ready to tell you what you need to know to keep 'em in their place.

They let me off easy this time, with just a bit of community service to perform. That's why I'm here; to help you better understand hazardous materials so you can protect yourself and safely respond to any hazardous situation that may develop in your college lab or your future career.

Remember that safety begins now, not when you get your first job. (That's right, someday you'll have a job!) By the time we get to the end of this guide, you'll have a solid understanding of:

- What makes a chemical hazardous
- Exposure limits
- How to recognize the physical and health hazards of chemicals
- How a material safety data sheet (MSDS) can be a valuable safety and reference tool
- General laboratory safety, including first aid and spill, leak, and disposal procedures
- The importance of using personal protective equipment
- Basics of laboratory protocol and safety techniques
- Regulations affecting the way that schools and colleges handle, store, and dispose of hazardous materials
- Environmental protection

. . . and I'll be jetting off to some remote island paradise.

Oh, I also have some tips for you. No, not gambling tips! (Boy, these Feds are so suspicious.) These are tips you can use to work safely with hazardous chemicals. I'm even gonna give you some pretty helpful profiles of more than 90 chemicals you'll probably come across in lab experiments. What can I say? I'm a great guy. To top it all off, I put together a glossary of over 500 terms and abbreviations associated with the use and potential hazards of chemicals commonly found in laboratories. Okay, so I didn't put it together myself, but it's pretty good, so I'm taking the credit for it.

First I'd like to tell you the story of how I finally got caught red-handed. The trouble all started several years ago. There was this bright-eyed young chemistry student, like yourself, who worked closely with hazardous materials. Too closely in fact, but she didn't realize it until she met me.

Cheryl entered her freshman lab not knowing what to expect, but curious. Unfortunately, she never learned how to safely work with hazardous materials. Her lab instructor required the students to wear lab coats, goggles, and gloves. Cheryl thought the coat was uncomfortable, the goggles pinched her nose, and the gloves made her hands sweat. Besides, she was only working with small amounts of chemicals, so why bother being careful, right? WRONG!

Like many students in her lab, Cheryl left her protective equipment on the bench whenever she could get away with it. Not very smart. Some of the chemicals used could do a lot of harm to her body, not to mention her clothing. Cheryl and her lab partners performed many experiments without questioning if the materials were toxic? corrosive? flammable? reactive? They never even read a material safety data sheet (MSDS). Have you? While it's true that not every material in your lab is hazardous, you need to know how to properly identify and safely handle the ones that are.

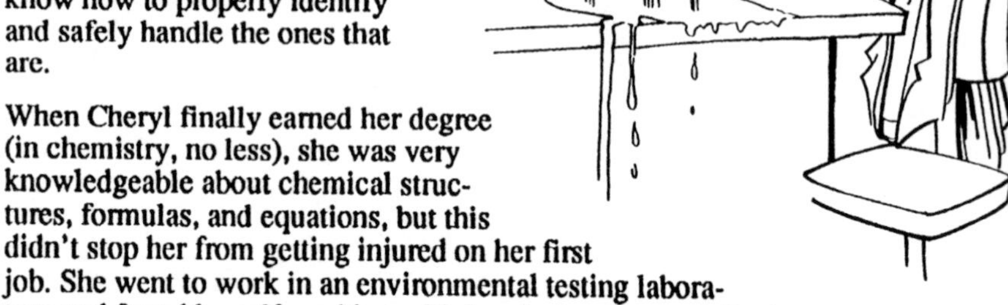

When Cheryl finally earned her degree (in chemistry, no less), she was very knowledgeable about chemical structures, formulas, and equations, but this didn't stop her from getting injured on her first job. She went to work in an environmental testing laboratory and found herself working with hundreds of potentially dangerous chemicals. Because she hadn't learned the principles of laboratory safety in college, she didn't realize the importance of protecting herself against these materials.

For example, she didn't know that there are different types of gloves, each one made with a *specific* material to protect the skin from contact with a *specific* class of chemicals. She didn't know that the rubber gloves she wore at work would protect her hands from dirt and water, but not from some solvents like kerosene, turpentine, or hexane.

That's where I come in. I was hangin' out in the lab, mixin' it up with some of my hexane buddies, when I rubbed up against Cheryl's glove. I traveled right through the glove and was absorbed into her skin. What a trip!

Over a period of time, and after many similar instances, called "long-term" or "chronic" exposure, I damaged Cheryl's nervous system. She went through a lot of pain and several doctors. (I feel pretty bad about it now.) The final diagnosis was "chemical overexposure". After medication and several years of suffering, Cheryl wiped me out of her system. That's when I was handed over to the Feds and brought to justice.

There ought to be a law

Why was Cheryl wearing improper safety equipment? Isn't there a law to protect laboratory employees from exposure? Well, there is a law, called the *Occupational Exposures to Hazardous Chemicals in Laboratories* standard.

This law requires employers to provide training and safety instruction as well as the appropriate protective equipment for employees. Unfortunately, Cheryl's employer was as unconcerned about safety as Cheryl was. The first and only time that her supervisor mentioned material safety was briefly during a required 35-minute orientation session held her first week on the job. It wasn't enough to break the bad habits that Cheryl had developed in school. Besides, she'd made it through four years of college without incident, so why start being cautious now, right? WRONG again!

As soon as Cheryl began doing lab work on her new job, her bad habits took over. When she did wear protective equipment, she never stopped to determine if it was the *proper* equipment. She grabbed whatever was readily available. That's how she ended up with the wrong gloves.

This whole situation could have been avoided if Cheryl had started learning about chemical safety when she took her first chemistry course. (And I'd still be free as a bird.) If she had understood the materials she worked with; what type of gloves or other protective equipment to wear; how to read an MSDS; what exposure limits are; the laws that protect students and employees; and had developed the ability to assess a potentially dangerous situation in the lab, she would have been better prepared and protected. She would have known the right questions to ask. This guide has been provided to help save you from making the same mistakes that Cheryl made.

No one expects you to know everything about hazardous materials; but it is important for you to know how to obtain the information you need - where to go and who to ask. Don't depend on the government, your school, or your employer to protect you. *Protect yourself.* Stick with me, and I'll tell you what you need to know. Remember, what you learn today will last you a lifetime. It will help create a safer, healthier, and better informed atmosphere for you and your classmates now, through your college years, and into your careers, whether you choose chemistry as an occupation, or any number of other career choices that involve hazardous materials.

It's pretty amazing how many occupations besides chemistry involve the use of hazardous materials. We really get around! Biologists, physicians, dentists, nurses, photographers, artists, computer designers, engineers, painters, carpenters, and more, all use hazardous materials in their work. In fact, you probably couldn't get along without us. It's so hard to be humble when you're in such demand.

Turn to Quiz on page 131.

II. What Makes a Chemical Hazardous?

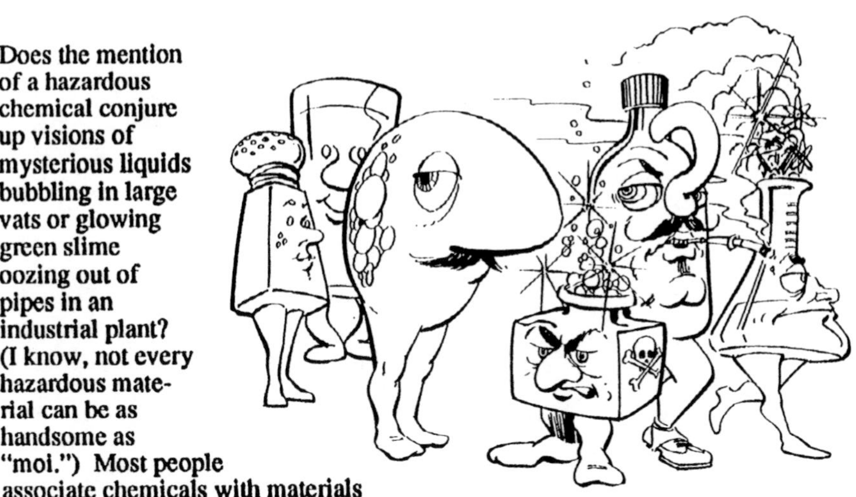

Does the mention of a hazardous chemical conjure up visions of mysterious liquids bubbling in large vats or glowing green slime oozing out of pipes in an industrial plant? (I know, not every hazardous material can be as handsome as "moi.") Most people associate chemicals with materials in bottles, cans, and drums produced by industry, but actually, all matter (the "stuff" composing the world) is chemical in nature. You can't get away from us. We're everywhere! However, all chemicals are not hazardous. For example, water (H_2O) and table salt (NaCl) are chemicals found in your daily lives, and they're not usually considered hazardous (the little wimps).

A chemical is considered hazardous if it is:

- Determined to be cancer-causing, toxic, corrosive, an irritant, a strong sensitizer, flammable, or reactive, and thereby poses a threat to health and the environment.
- Specifically listed under the *Occupational Safety and Health Act*, 29 CFR part 1910, Subpart Z.
- Assigned a threshold limit value (TLV) by the American Conference of Governmental Industrial Hygienists (ACGIH).

There are many chemicals, both nonhazardous and hazardous, that you routinely encounter. You need to be aware of the hazardous ones, especially in your lab courses. Here's how chemicals can enter your body and cause all kinds of damage:

Routes of Entry

Inhalation

Gases and Vapors

As gases and vapors, the nose and mouth are the first places we go for. Believe me, it's not the most pleasant trip (I much prefer the Bahamas), but it's the best route to our ultimate destination, the lungs. Inhalation is the most likely route of exposure for chemicals because whatever is contained in the air you breathe may enter your lungs. Once in the lungs, air contaminants can easily enter the bloodstream and circulate through your body.

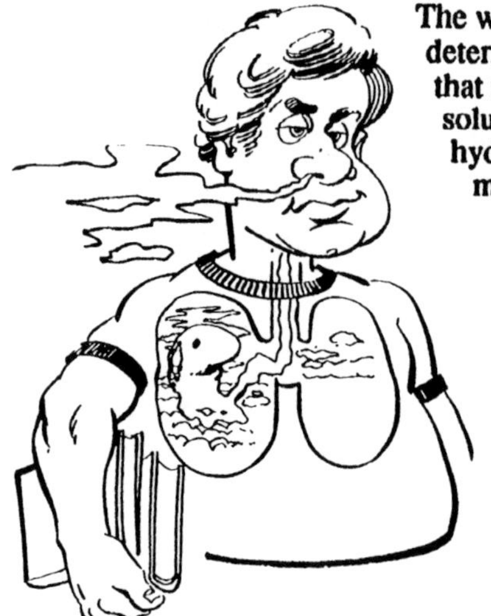

The water solubility of a gas or vapor can determine the amount of inhaled material that reaches your lungs. Highly water soluble gases, such as ammonia and hydrogen chloride, readily dissolve in the moisture found in the nose and upper respiratory tract, causing irritation. And this irritation can be much worse than just an itchy or runny nose.

What about water insoluble gases? (Just when you thought it was safe to breathe.) Even though insoluble gases, such as nitrogen dioxide and phosgene, are not absorbed at the upper respiratory sites, they can easily reach the lungs and cause severe irritation, such as pulmonary edema (fluid in the lungs). Now for the double whammy - some gases, such as carbon monoxide, reach the lungs, absorb into the bloodstream, and then circulate through your system to affect other parts of your body. You think that's bad, wait 'til I tell you about my nasty cousins, dusts and fumes.

Particulate Matter

Everyone knows what dust is, but I'm not talking about the kind that's taken over your dorm room. (Aaachoo!) When inhaled, particulate matter, such as dust from powdered solids or fumes from burning chemicals, can also cause damage. Particle size can determine what region of the respiratory system the inhaled material reaches and the subsequent injury that can result. Larger particles (10 μ, μ=micron) can get caught up in your nose hairs and never reach the lungs. (Let's hear it for the nose hairs!) Smaller particles (1 to 5 μ) can sneak past the nose hairs and continue to travel through the nose, down the throat, and to the airways, where they become trapped in mucous. The mucous containing the inhaled particles is moved up to the throat by tiny hairs called cilia. The particles are then either swallowed or coughed up. (Yum.) Now here comes another whammy. Even if the particles are swallowed and don't reach the lungs, they may still be harmful if they're absorbed through the gastrointestinal tract. Gotcha! Finally, the smallest particles (less than 1 μ) travel to the air sacs (alveoli) in the lungs where the blood picks up oxygen. This is where the fun really begins. Alveolar macrophages engulf the inhaled particles and destroy them (kinda like Pac Man). However, some particles, such as crystalline silica, asbestos, and beryllium, remain in the alveoli indefinitely to cause respiratory disease and even cancer.

Eye Contact

Now I want to get into your eyes and under your skin. Hey, that would make a great love song! (hmmm...hmmm...get into your eyes...hmmm... hmmm) Oh, sorry. Anyway, eye contact with a chemical can cause irritation or even permanent blindness, and that is nothing to sing about. Major eye injuries occur when the eye is perforated, burned by heat or contact with chemicals, or disrupted by a blow.

Like your lungs, your eyes also have some natural defenses: bony structures surrounding the eyes can protect against blows; eyebrows can divert fluids from flowing into your eyes; eyelids can close quickly to prevent particles from entering your eyes; and tears can dilute irritants that enter your eyes. However (there's always a catch), this protection is not enough, especially when handling chemicals. Always wear safety glasses, goggles, and/or a face shield when handling hazardous chemicals to avoid eye contact.

Skin Contact/Absorption

It's time to get really personal and talk about your skin. It consists of cells and tissues made of molecules of proteins, fatty substances called lipids, and carbohydrates. Like your skin, chemicals also consist of tiny molecules. When hazardous chemicals touch your skin, they react with your body's chemical components on a molecular level, and disrupt protein and lipid structures. This can result in local irritation and rashes, chemical burns, and/or permanent damage. Some chemicals not only cause local effects, they penetrate through the pores and layers of skin, like when I took that detour through Cheryl's skin.

When absorbed, a hazardous chemical can enter the bloodstream and damage organ systems such as your nerves, liver, kidneys, or red blood cells. Also, some hazardous chemicals penetrate the skin and cause an allergic reaction or sensitization. This means that each time you come in contact with that particular chemical, the reaction reoccurs and is often more severe.

Ingestion

Although it's highly unlikely that you would purposely nibble on a little phenolphthalein for lunch, accidental ingestion can occur. You can ingest small amounts of material by eating, drinking, smoking, biting your fingernails, even licking your finger to turn a page, with hands that are contaminated with chemicals in the lab. Watch out for chemicals such as lead, mercury, cyanide, and arsenic. While the amounts you swallow may be small, these chemicals can cause toxic effects or even kill you.

How Much of Me Can You Possibly Stand?

The amount of chemical absorbed into the body is referred to as dose. A dose depends on the chemical's strength or concentration, the length of exposure (duration), and how often (frequency) the exposure occurs. For example, when you're doing some late-night or early morning cramming for a major exam, you might prescribe for yourself the following dose: one extra strong pot of coffee (concentration) to be taken at hourly intervals (frequency) until you bounce off the walls on your way to class and successfully answer 50 multiple choice and 3 essays within seven minutes (duration). (The Feds do not recommend this method, nor would most doctors.)

For almost all chemicals, the greater the dose, the more severe the health effects. Some chemicals are more toxic (poisonous) than others. The more toxic a substance is, the smaller the dose required to affect your health. For example, to harm your body, lead requires a much smaller dose than many other chemicals because it's highly toxic. You may already have some lead in your blood due to its widespread presence in the environment. Gotcha again! Fortunately for most of you, this dose is too low to cause lead poisoning. Children, however, can be harmed by exposure to much lower doses of lead than adults.

Acute and Chronic Exposures

Exposure to a hazardous material for a brief period of time, such as minutes, hours, or several days, is referred to as "acute exposure". Health effects from acute exposures develop very rapidly. Exposure to a hazardous material over several months, years, or decades is referred to as "chronic exposure". Chronic effects are particularly dangerous because you may not experience discomfort in the presence of the material, but you may develop severe health problems later in life as a result of your exposure. It's kind of like a new car; one rain storm doesn't damage the shiny exterior, but constant exposure to the elements can result in a rusty hunk of junk. Because of the delay (latency period) between the time you suffer the chronic exposure and the time your health problems become apparent, your exposures may be overlooked as a possible cause of your current condition.

Protect Yourself

Hazardous materials are notorious for affecting people in different ways. Everyone has a different level of tolerance. Your age, size, sex, physical condition, and exposure level to other substances, such as drugs, tobacco, and alcohol, determine how much exposure your body can safely tolerate. Whenever possible, stay *well below* permissible exposure levels.

Always take appropriate measures to protect yourself. To reduce exposure, engineering controls (ventilation, laboratory hoods, etc.) are better than administrative controls (warning labels, signs on cans and bottles, and training), and administrative controls are better than personal protective equipment (gloves, aprons, safety glasses, etc.). However, sometimes a combination of all three controls is necessary to effectively reduce overall exposure. For example, if you want to avoid inhaling vapors produced during a reaction, perform the reaction in the hood. This protects you against inhalation, but it's also a good idea to wear gloves, safety goggles, a lab coat, and other necessary equipment to protect yourself against contact with the chemicals you're using to create the reaction.

Turn to Quiz on page 133.

III. Exposure Limits

I'm about to hit you with a bunch of acronyms and abbreviations and definitions on exposure limits. Sit up straight, get your feet off the desk, and TURN OFF THAT STEREO ALREADY!

And whatever you do, don't read this section right before you doze off for the night. Otherwise, you might find yourself lost in a dark maze where you're being pursued by the meanest bunch of exposure limits you've ever run across. First, there's the giant IDLH creature with fangs the size of hedge clippers. You run away as fast as you can, until you come to a fork in the maze. You make a quick left, only to be attacked by TLVs that pelt you with STELs, TWAs, and TLV-Cs. Suddenly, a light appears ahead, and you take off in that direction. As you emerge from the darkness, the ground disappears beneath you. You fall, passing by floating LD_{LO}, LD_{50}, LC_{LO}, LC_{50}, and TD_{LO}, who laugh as you descend. Then, a great hand reaches out and catches you, and you wake up in your bed, realizing that you were "saved by the PEL"!

Okay, so it's not the best punch line in the world, but there is a moral to the story. If you don't acquire a good working knowledge of these definitions, you may be left in the dark, and they will continue to chase you down and intimidate rather than protect you. However, if you follow my lead, you'll learn why it's so important to your safety and health to know these exposure limit definitions. First, here's a bit of background information.

The Occupational Safety and Health Administration (OSHA) lists approximately 450 substances as air contaminants. Many of these substances are commonly used in lab work. OSHA limits exposure by inhalation of the vapors, dusts, or mists of these air contaminants by establishing permissible exposure limits (PELs). Unlike other recommended exposure guidelines, such as the American Conference of Governmental Industrial Hygienists (ACGIH) threshold limit values (TLVs) and the National Institute of Occupational Safety and Health (NIOSH) recommended exposure limits (RELs), OSHA PELs have the power of law.

These acronyms can be pretty confusing at first . . . here a PEL, there a REL. Boy! Leave it to the humans to make things so complicated. Oops, I forgot who I was talking to. Just kidding.

Hubie is here to save the day. I'll lead you through the twists and turns of this mysterious maze of exposure limits meanings. I'm thinkin' of joining up with the Feds, and this is my test mission. If I can lead you safely through this maze, I'm in for sure. And like any good investigating team, we've got to put our heads together. My job is to feed you the information, definition by definition. Your job is to consider the importance of each definition, understand its impact on your safety, and put it to use in your lab work.

Most of the exposure limits we'll be investigating are guidelines, not absolute boundaries between safe and hazardous conditions. Think of them as the speed limit signs posted on the roads you travel. Speed limits are laws put in place to protect drivers and pedestrians. If a road restricts you to 55 mph, no reasonable person would say that traveling 54 mph is guaranteed to keep you out of an accident. On the other hand, no reasonable person believes that driving 56 mph on the same road will automatically result in an accident. I think we can agree, however, that the faster you go above the speed limit, the greater your chance of having an accident. It's also true that if you exceed the speed limit, you're breaking the law. People who violate the speed limit are asking for trouble, and they're likely to find it, maybe not the first time, or even the second, but some day.

The same theory applies to most exposure limits. There's no guarantee that if your exposure to a hazardous substance exceeds the limits, you'll automatically experience an adverse health effect. However, you can't assume that if you're exposed to permissible levels of a substance, you won't suffer adverse effects.

Okay, it's time to plow our way through those definitions. Ready? Hang on, here we go!

OSHA

PEL
Permissible Exposure Limit
The allowable limit for an air contaminant to which nearly all workers may be repeatedly exposed day after day without adverse health effects. A PEL may also be expressed as a time-weighted average (TWA), a short-term exposure limit (STEL), or ceiling limit (C).

C
Ceiling
The employee's exposure which shall not be exceeded during any part of the workday.

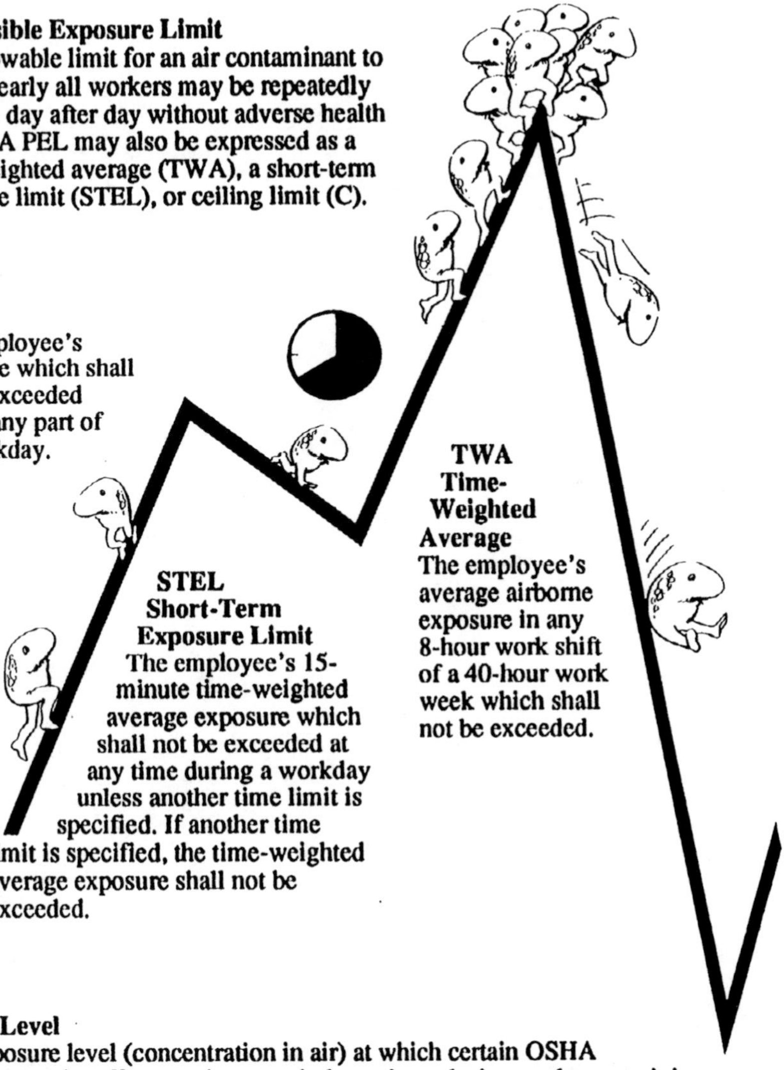

STEL
Short-Term Exposure Limit
The employee's 15-minute time-weighted average exposure which shall not be exceeded at any time during a workday unless another time limit is specified. If another time limit is specified, the time-weighted average exposure shall not be exceeded.

TWA
Time-Weighted Average
The employee's average airborne exposure in any 8-hour work shift of a 40-hour work week which shall not be exceeded.

AL
Action Level
The exposure level (concentration in air) at which certain OSHA regulations take effect, such as workplace air analysis, employee training, medical monitoring, and recordkeeping. Exposure at or above action level is termed occupational exposure. Exposure below this level can also be harmful. This level is generally half the PEL.

ACGIH

TLV

Threshold Limit Value

The American Conference of Governmental Industrial Hygienists (ACGIH) has determined TLVs for almost 600 substances. A TLV represents the recommended air concentration levels of hazardous substances to which nearly all workers may be repeatedly exposed day after day without adverse health effects. The TLVs are established for the "average person", equating to a 150 pound male, age 25-44. TLVs are generally reviewed and updated annually. There are different types of TLV measurements. You'll know what type you're dealing with by checking the word or abbreviation that follows TLV.

TLV-TWA

Threshold Limit Value - Time-Weighted Average

The time-weighted average concentration for a normal 8-hour workday and a 40-hour work week to which workers may be repeatedly exposed, day after day, without adverse effect.

TLV-STEL

Threshold Limit Value - Short-Term Exposure Limit

The maximum concentration to which workers can be exposed for a continuous period of 15 minutes, without the probability of experiencing irritation, chronic or irreversible damage, or narcosis (stupor or unconsciousness) to a sufficient degree. The daily TLV-TWA still may not be exceeded and only four 15-minute exposures per day are permitted with at least 60 minutes between exposure periods. If warranted by observed biological effects, an averaging period other than 15 minutes may be recommended.

TLV-C

Threshold Limit Value - Ceiling

The concentration not to be exceeded during any part of the working exposure. Unlike other TLVs, a TLV-C is more than a guideline, it's a definite boundary.

NIOSH

The National Institute of Occupational Safety and Health (NIOSH) also prepares exposure limit guidelines for hazardous materials. The goal for NIOSH is to research and recommend the exposure limits intended to reduce or eliminate adverse health and safety effects of hazardous substances or conditions in the workplace. NIOSH airborne concentration limits are expressed as:

REL
Recommended Exposure Limit
The highest allowable airborne concentration that is not expected to injure a person. RELs may be expressed as ceiling limits or time-weighted average concentrations for up to a 10-hour workday during a 40-hour work week.

IDLH
Immediately Dangerous to Life and Health
The maximum concentration from which, in the event of a respirator failure, a worker could escape within 30 minutes without any escape-impairing symptoms or irreversible health effects. IDLH values are used to determine the selection of an appropriate respirator.

Toxicity Data

The hazard of a material depends on its toxicity, the way the material is used, the amount of exposure the person experiences, and the individual's personal response. Using laboratory animals in controlled experiments, toxicity data is generated to help determine a chemical's potentially adverse effect on humans and to provide guidelines for establishing exposure limits. Since animal and human metabolisms differ, expert interpretation and judgment are essential for applying animal toxicity data to human chemical exposure. Health and safety professionals determine how much of a particular substance most people can be exposed to, over how long a period of time without adverse reactions, and then set exposure limits based on the toxicity data.

On the following pages you will find toxicity terms that you should know:

LC_{50}
Lethal Concentration 50
The concentration of a material in air that, on the basis of laboratory tests, is expected to kill 50% of a group of test animals when administered as a single respiratory exposure in a specific time period.

LC_{LO}
Lethal Concentration Low
The lowest concentration of substance in air reported to have caused death in humans or animals. The reported concentrations may be entered for periods of exposure that are less than 24 hours (acute) or greater than 24 hours (subacute ar chronic).

LD_{50}
Lethal Dose 50
The single dose of substance that causes the death of 50% of an animal populatic from exposure to a substance by any route other than inhalation.

LD_{LO}
Lethal Dose Low
The lowest dose of a substance introduced by any route, other than inhalation, reported to have caused death in humans or animals.

TC_{LO}
Toxic Concentration Low
The lowest concentration of substance in air to which humans or animals have been exposed for any given period of time that has produced any toxic effect in humans or produced any tumorigenic or reproductive effect in animals or human

TD_{LO}
Toxic Dose Low
The lowest dose of a substance introduced by any route other than inhalation ove any given period of time and reported to produce any toxic effect in humans or to produce any tumorigenic or reproductive effect in animals or humans.

Since most limits express concentration of hazardous materials in the air, the uni of measurement used must be appropriate. You will find that most exposure level are expressed in one of two ways:

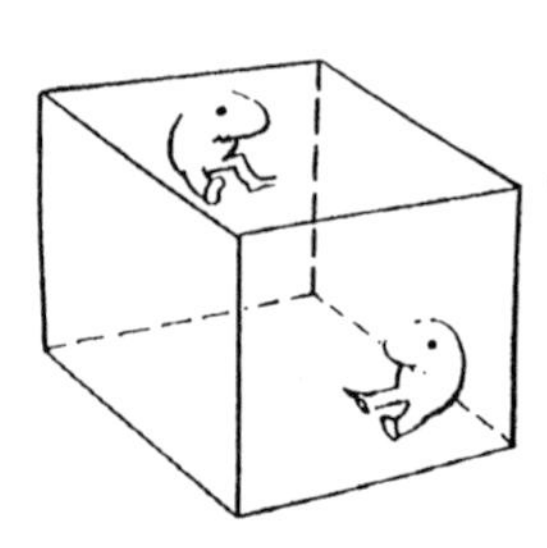

mg/m^3
Milligrams per Cubic Meter of Air
A common unit for measuring concentrations of particulates (minute separate particles). For example, a TLV-TWA of 5 mg/m^3 will mean that 5 milligrams of the substance per cubic meter of air has been determined to pose no hazard to an average person during a normal 8-hour workday or 40-hour work week;

$$mg / m^3 = \frac{ppm \times \text{molecular weight}}{24.45}$$

ppm
Parts Per Million
The common unit for measuring the concentration of a gas or vapor in air; ppm is defined as "parts of vapor or gas per million parts of air by volume at 25 °C and 1 atm pressure" (ACGIH);

$$\text{ppm} = \frac{\text{mg} / \text{m}^3 \times 24.45}{\text{molecular weight}}$$

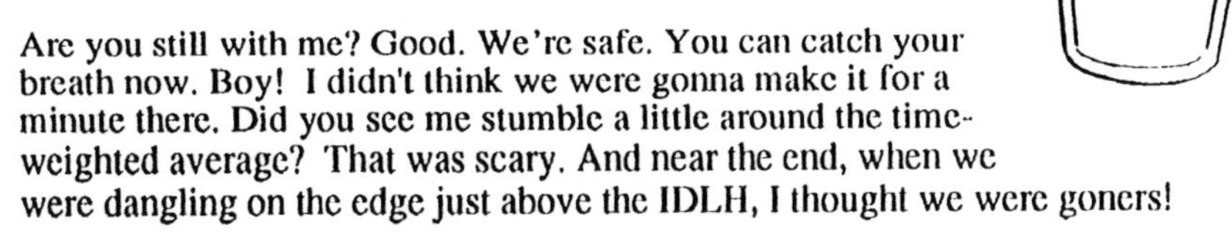

Are you still with me? Good. We're safe. You can catch your breath now. Boy! I didn't think we were gonna make it for a minute there. Did you see me stumble a little around the time-weighted average? That was scary. And near the end, when we were dangling on the edge just above the IDLH, I thought we were goners!

Now I don't expect you to memorize every piece of information you just read. (Your instructor might, but I don't.) The important thing is that you made it through, and in doing so, have become more familiar with these important terms. And besides, it gave me a chance to prove myself. The Feds are pretty impressed with my leadership skills. I told them I was good.

Turn to Quiz on page 135.

IV. Recognizing the Physical and Health Hazards of Chemicals

How do you know if a chemical is hazardous? Some materials may look alike, smell alike, even react alike, but they can have potential hazards that are very different.

I'd like to introduce you to some friends of mine. Up front are a couple of crazy liquids, A.C. Tone and Ben Zene. Behind them are two of my most solid friends, Al Uminum and Nick L. Chloride. And way back there are two of the wildest gases I know, R. Gon and Ray Don. (But you can call him Ray, or you can call him Don, or you can . . .)

Now you can definitely tell the difference between liquids, solids, and gases, right? But what about two liquids like A.C. Tone (acetone) and Ben Zene (benzene)? They're both colorless and smell sweet. I've known these guys for years and I still can't tell them apart. You'd think their mothers would stop dressing them alike!

Acetone is a dangerous fire and explosion hazard (a real hothead). Inhalation of high concentrations may produce narcosis (unconsciousness). Prolonged or repeated skin contact causes dryness, irritation, and mild dermatitis. Benzene is also a dangerous fire and explosion hazard. The biggest difference between the two is that benzene is a confirmed human carcinogen by the IARC (International Agency for Research on Cancer). Chronic low-level exposure may cause cancer (leukemia) and bone marrow damage, with injury to blood-forming tissue. Boy, and I thought ol' Benny was a nice guy.

When working with hazardous chemicals in the lab, you must know exactly what substance you're working with. You must also recognize the potential hazards of chemicals before you handle them. On the following pages, you'll find some of the most common hazard warnings. This listing includes the hazard warning symbols, a brief description, and examples of chemicals that fall into these categories. Continually look for these warnings in your work. Never expose yourself to any material unless you know exactly what it is, how it can hurt you, and what you need to protect yourself.

Common Hazard Warnings

The following are only examples:

FLAMMABLE

Describes any solid, liquid, vapor, or gas that can be ignited readily and, when ignited, burns so vigorously and persistently as to create a serious hazard. The DOT defines a flammable liquid as a liquid with a flash point of not more than 141 °F (60.5 °C).

Acetone
Acetic Acid, Glacial
Amyl Nitrate
Benzene
Carbon Disulfide
Cyclohexane
Ethanol
Methanol
Isopropyl Alcohol

CORROSIVE

A liquid or solid that causes visible destruction of, or irreversible alterations in, living tissue by chemical action at the site of contact; or a liquid that causes a severe corrosion rate on steel or aluminum.

Ammonia, Aqueous
Nitric Acid
Phosphoric Acid
Potassium Chromate
Glacial Acetic Acid
Hydrochloric Acid
Hydrogen Fluoride
Potassium Hydroxide
Sodium Hydroxide
Sulfuric Acid

You've got me under your skin.

COMPRESSED GAS

Any material contained under pressure, i.e. dissolved gas or liquefied by compression or refrigeration. Refrigerated gases may cause frostbite on contact.

Ammonia, Anhydrous
Argon
Carbon Dioxide
Chlorine
Chlorodifluoromethane
Nitrogen
Sulfur Dioxide

No, you don't get three wishes, wise guy.

POISONOUS MATERIAL

A material, other than a gas, that is known (on the basis of animal tests) to be so toxic to humans or causes such extreme irritation as to afford a hazard to health.

Aniline
Arsenic Trichloride
Calcium Cyanide
Carbon Tetrachloride
Chloroform
Mercury (II) Chloride
Methyl Isocyanate
Nitrobenzene
Phenol
Toluene Diisocyanate

Here lies Hubie
Whose life was
happy and stable
Until the day he forgot
To read the label.

EXPLOSIVE

A material that produces a sudden, almost instantaneous release of pressure, gas, and heat when subjected to abrupt shock, pressure, or high temperature.

Ammonium Perchlorate
Ammonium Picrate
Barium Azide
Picric Acid
TNT (Trinitrotoluene)
Tetrazol-1-Acetic Acid

That's the last time
I eat Mexican food.

PYROPHORIC

Describes a material even in a small quantity that, without an external ignition source, can ignite within five minutes after coming in contact with air.

Activated Carbon
Aluminum Alkyl
Halides
Aluminum Alkyl
Hydride
Aluminum Borohydride
Magnesium Powder
Pentaborane
Phosphorus
(yellow or white)
Uranium Metal
Zinc Powder
Zirconium Powder

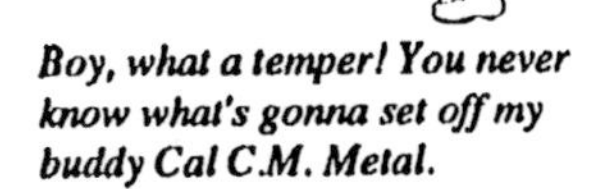

Boy, what a temper! You never know what's gonna set off my buddy Cal C.M. Metal.

WATER REACTIVE

Describes a material that by contact with water becomes spontaneously flammable or gives off a flammable or toxic gas and presents a health hazard.

And people wonder why I never take a shower.

- Barium
- Calcium, Metal
- Iron (III) Chloride
- Lithium
- Magnesium Powder
- Potassium Hydroxide
- Potassium, Metal
- Sodium Hydroxide
- Sulfuric Acid
- Zinc Powder

COMBUSTIBLE

A term the DOT and others use to classify certain materials with low flash points that ignite easily. The DOT defines a combustible liquid as a liquid with a flash point above 141 °F (60.5 °C) and below 200 °F (93 °C).

- 2-Amino-1-Butanol
- Aniline
- Benzaldehyde
- Butyric Acid
- Camphor
- Cyclohexanol
- Diethylene Glycol Monobutyl Ether
- Methylene Diisocyanate
- Phenol
- 1-Propanol

Is that starve a cold and feed a fever, or the other way around?

CARCINOGEN

A material that either causes cancer in humans, or, because it causes cancer in animals, is considered capable of causing cancer in humans.

- Acrylonitrile
- Asbestos
- Benzene
- Carbon Tetrachloride
- Formaldehyde
- Lead, Inorganic
- PCBs
- Perchloroethylene
- Styrene
- Toluene-2,4-Diisocyanate

INFECTIOUS SUBSTANCE

A viable microorganism, or its toxin, which causes or may cause disease in humans or animals.

Meet my cousin, Cyrus the Virus.

Bacteria
HIV
Parasites
Rabies
Viral Hepatitis
Viruses

OXIDIZER AND OXIDIZING AGENT

The DOT defines an oxidizer as a substance that yields oxygen readily to cause or enhance the combustion (oxidation) of organic matter. An oxidizer is a significant hazard in a fire situation. Contact may cause caustic burns.

Ammonium Dichromate
Ammonium Nitrate
Hydrogen Peroxide
Lead Nitrate
Nitric Acid
Potassium Nitrate
Potassium Permanganate
Silver Nitrate
Sodium Nitrate

Air fresheners are the least of my problems.

RADIOACTIVE

A source of ionizing rays produced by the disintegration of atomic nuclei. Overexposure of living tissue to ionizing radiation results in cellular damage.

Carbon-14
Gallium-65
Hafnium-170
Krypton-74
Niobium-96
Osmium-180
Phosphorus-32
Plutonium-234
Rubidium-79
Thorium-227
Tritium
Uranium-230

I think I feel a migraine coming on.

Turn to Quiz on page 137.

V. Material Safety Data Sheets

Hazard warnings bring your attention to the immediate danger, but the best way to get the complete scoop on the hazardous members of my family tree is to read a material safety data sheet (MSDS). (Or you could talk to my Aunt Ether. What a gossip!) An MSDS is every hazardous material's worst nightmare (and so's my Aunt Ether). It's your ultimate weapon in significantly cutting down the threat of us hazardous materials doing you harm. It's like water to the Wicked Witch of the West, or Kryptonite to Superman.

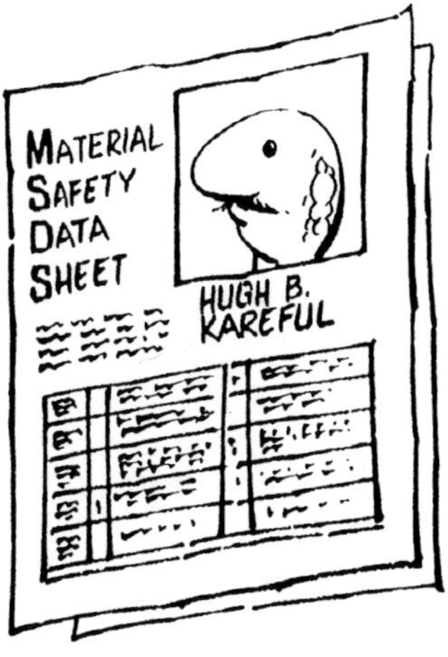

The more informed you are about hazardous materials, the less intimidating and mysterious we become. Each material safety data sheet is like an "unauthorized" biography on a hazardous material. Why, the one they did on me is downright embarrassing! It reveals all my secrets, like any alias I might use (I have several), where I can be found, how I react in certain situations, and worst of all, how to safely dispose of me!

The main objective of MSDSs, like everything else we've discussed, is to protect you. They provide concise information about the hazards of the materials you work with so that you can protect yourself and respond to emergency situations.

The MSDS Format

MSDSs were initially written for health and safety professionals and trained workers in the chemical industry. The information was usually pretty technical, and the type of information and formats varied from supplier to supplier. As Federal and state right-to-know regulations expanded (much to my family's dismay), a wider audience with diverse backgrounds needed MSDSs. Like anything else, increase the number of people involved, and you'll increase the confusion just as much. Reading and understanding the various MSDSs became an even more difficult task. That's when the Chemical Manufacturers Association (CMA) stepped in and began working on a standard to develop *consistent* and *understandable* MSDSs that would be easily recognized in the U.S., Canada, and Europe. This standard, also accepted by ANSI (American National Standards Institute), does not fulfill every country's legal requirements, but it does provide *consistent* and *useful* information to a variety of audiences, from the worker on the shop floor to the physician treating an exposure victim. Specific legal requirements for an MSDS in the U.S. are addressed in OSHA's *Hazard Communication* standard, and are covered in the first 10 of 16 total sections of the proposed

ANSI standard. It's not yet known whether OSHA will adopt the ANSI standar and revise the *Hazard Communication* standard. Remember, ANSI standards, although well-respected and followed by most industries, are *recommendations* Only OSHA is *law* in these parts, partner.

Currently, according to OSHA's *Hazard Communication* standard, MSDSs mu include:

- The material's identity, including its chemical and common names (examp brand name: *Clorox*™; chemical name: *sodium hypochlorite*; common nam *bleach*).
- Hazardous ingredients (even in parts as small as 1%).
- Cancer-causing ingredients (even in parts as small as 0.1%).
- List of physical and chemical hazards (stability, reactivity) and characteristics (flammable, explosive, corrosive, etc.).
- List of health hazards, including:
  - *Acute effects* such as burns or unconsciousness, which occur immediately.
  - *Chronic effects* such as allergic sensitization, skin problems, or respiratory disease, which build up over a period of time.
- If the material is listed as a carcinogen by OSHA, IARC, or NTP.
- Limits to which a worker can be exposed, the primary routes of entry into t body, specific target organs likely to sustain damage, and medical problems that can be aggravated by exposure.
- Precautions and safety equipment.
- Emergency and first aid procedures.
- Specific fire-fighting information.
- Procedures for cleanup of spills and leaks.
- Precautions for safe handling and use, including personal hygiene.
- Identity of the organization responsible for creating the MSDS, date of issu and emergency phone number.

The last six sections of the ANSI standard include toxicological (animal data), ecological, disposal, transport, and regulatory information, as well as a section for other information. Because these last sections are not required by OSHA, manufacturers may choose not to include this information on their MSDSs. However, this information may be required internationally. For consistency, the ANSI standard recommends that the headings be listed even in the absence of data, and that the company print either *data not given* or *data not available*. The ANSI standard also allows some flexibility in placing the information within the 16 sections. For example, exposure guidelines, such as OSHA PELs or ACGIH TLVs, may be placed in Section 2 - Composition/Information on Ingredients, or in Section 8 - Exposure Controls/Personal Protection.

An understanding of how to interpret the data on the MSDS is your best defense against accidents and injuries. Knowing what data an MSDS should include, as well as where it's included, will help you find it more quickly.

Reading an MSDS

On the following pages are descriptions of the sixteen sections of an MSDS according to the ANSI standard, and explanations that will help you find and interpret the information.

Section 1. Chemical Product and Company Identification

Information In This Section. Section 1 provides the name, address, and telephone number of the company that produced the material, the MSDS's date of issue (or most recent revision), and the name of the material. The name of the material on the MSDS must be spelled exactly as it is on the container you received.

If one generic MSDS is used to cover various grades of a material, all grades must be listed as well as any known synonyms. If an optional number or code is used by the manufacturer to help identify the MSDS, it should appear in this section, and on every consecutive page of the MSDS.

Why This Information Is Important. Thousands of materials with many similar names are found in workplaces. A mistake on the supplier's part in sending the wrong sheet needs to be caught immediately, before workers put their trust in the wrong information. In addition, having the supplier's telephone number on the sheet can be a vital time-saver in the event of an accident involving the material or for requesting additional data.

Section 2. Composition/Information on Ingredients

Information In This Section. Section 2 lists the product's individual hazardous chemicals and their relative percentages. The material's corresponding CAS (Chemical Abstracts Service) No.(s) must also be listed. All ingredients that meet the OSHA *Hazard Communication* standard criteria of a hazardous ingredient must be identified here.

Manufacturers may also choose to list active ingredients, significant ingredients regulated under other Federal, state, or local regulations, or a complete ingredient disclosure, including nonhazardous components. Complex mixtures recognized as single substances may be listed as single components. If any of the hazardous components is a trade secret, this will be indicated in lieu of identifying the component. Suppliers of such products must still provide health hazard data on the MSDS and additional information to safety professionals who have a documentable need to know.

My chiropractor hates it when I do this.

If established, the chemical's exposure limits are shown. For example, the phrase "8-hr TWA: 100 ppm or 300 mg/m^3" is a guideline establishing an exposure level that should not be exceeded when averaged over an eight-hour workday. See TWA in **Section III.** *Note:* Exposure limit information may alternatively be found in Section 8.

Why This Information Is Important. Exposure to certain hazardous materials may be acceptable, but only for periods of time not to exceed certain limits and a concentrations of the material no greater than certain limits. These limits are found on the MSDS. If a job involves exposure for greater periods of time or at higher concentrations, the worker will know that wearing protective clothing or taking other protective measures as described on the MSDS is vital to their health.

Exposure levels are set for healthy adult workers, based on the average 150 lb male, age 25-44. Lower exposure levels are necessary for people at higher risk; i.e., those who are young or elderly, pregnant, smokers, etc., or workers who have already been exposed to other materials for which exposure limits have been set. Exertion increases the effects of exposure. See Body Burden on page 93.

Exposure to more than one hazardous substance at a time can be especially harmful, because the combined effects of more than one material can prove more damaging than the additive effects of each material (e.g. 2 + 2 = 10). This is called synergy. For example, both smoking and exposure to asbestos can cause lung cancer; however, if a smoker is also exposed to asbestos, the danger of lung cancer is far greater than just adding together the separate risks from the two exposures.

Section 3. Hazards Identification

Information In This Section. Section 3 is divided into two parts. The first part describes the material's appearance and gives an overview of the most significant immediate concerns for emergency personnel. For example:

Chlorine is a greenish-yellow gas with a pungent, suffocating odor. It is a highly toxic and corrosive gas which is irritating to the eyes and mucous membranes. Although noncombustible, it is a strong oxidizer that supports the combustion of other organic materials. It is an extremely reactive and explosive gas. Chlorine reacts with many common substances such as acetylene, ammonia, hydrogen, ether, fuel gas, hydrocarbons, turpentine, and finely divided metals.

If a material is considered a confirmed or probable carcinogen by IARC, NTP, or OSHA, a teratogen, a mutagen, toxic to aquatic life or a danger to the environment, this may also be included in the emergency overview. (*Note:* This information may also be found in Section 2, 15, or 16.)

The second part of Section 3 provides information on the potential adverse health effects and symptoms associated with exposure to the material, its components, or known by-products. Exposure to a harmful chemical can occur through several routes of entry into the body, including eye contact, skin contact, inhalation, and ingestion (swallowing). Section 3 of the MSDS must list all of the routes of entry pertinent to this material. Acute (short-term) and chronic (long-term) health effects, symptoms of exposure, and medical conditions aggravated by exposure must be stated. If the material is carcinogenic, that fact must be stated.

Why This Information Is Important. Sickness and even death from improper exposure to certain materials can be prevented if the potential hazards are known ahead of time. Chronic effects are particularly dangerous because a worker may not experience discomfort in the presence of the material, but may develop severe health problems later in life as a result of the exposures. Some materials harm a particular organ of the body, and such "target organs" (heart, liver, lungs, kidneys, etc.) would be listed.

Inhalation. The principal route of entry into the body is through inhalation. Not all materials that are bad for you actually have strong or bad odors. Many dangerous chemicals have very little odor or have the ability to quickly fatigue the sense of smell so that you are no longer aware of the odor but are still being hurt through exposure to toxic concentrations.

Who needs an amusement park?

Contact and Ingestion. Some materials can pass right through the skin to react with body tissue and be absorbed into the internal organs. Eye contact with some materials (dust, liquid splashes, or solution vapor or mist) can be irritating or even cause permanent damage, resulting in blindness.

Section 3 will only list animal data if it's considered relevant to human health. For example, if a material was found nontoxic in animal studies, this may be stated here. Alternatively, if a material has no human case studies or epidemiological data on which to base its toxicity, animal studies may be quoted, i.e. *based on animal testing, this material is presumed to...* Detailed animal data may be found in Section 11 - Toxicological Information.

Section 4. First Aid Measures

Information In This Section. Section 4 describes medical and first aid treatments for accidental exposure by route of exposure (i.e., inhalation, skin, eye, ingestion). Any known antidotes that may be administered by a lay person or specially trained personnel will be indicated.

A subsection entitled *Note to Physicians* may also be here. This will convey specific medical information on treatment and diagnostic procedures to trained medical personnel.

Why This Information Is Important. Professional medical treatment should be obtained as soon as possible after an accident. However, actions taken in the first few minutes after an exposure can make the difference between a minor and a major injury. For example, if you splash battery acid in your eyes, the more quickly you begin washing out your eyes with water, the more likely you are to save your eyesight. You should know the first aid measures for a material before you work with it.

Section 5. Fire-Fighting Measures

Don't try this at home, folks. I'm a professional.

Information In This Section. Section 5 of the MSDS provides basic fire-fighting guidance for trained fire fighters, emergency responders, employees, and occupational health and safety professionals. It describes the fire and explosive properties of the material, the proper extinguishing materials, and the precautions and procedures to safely and effectively fight the fire.

Why This Information Is Important. The flammable properties combined with the physical and chemical properties in Section 9 give a good indication of how hazardous a material is in a fire situation. Knowing this information, before fighting a fire, helps with preplanning response procedures and equipment.

The flash point is the lowest temperature at which a flammable liquid gives off enough vapor to form an ignitable mixture with air. At a glance you can tell from a low flash point that a material represents a fire hazard; for example, the flash point of gasoline is -43 °C (-45 °F). The autoignition temperature tells you how hot a material must be before it will set itself on fire without a flame or spark. Explosive or flammable limits [i.e. lower explosive limit (LEL) and upper explosive limit (UEL)] are the minimum and maximum concentrations of a flammable gas or vapor (percent by volume in air) between which an explosion can occur if an ignition source is present.

With most fires, the greatest danger to human life comes not from the heat of the flames, but from the often toxic smoke that can quickly fill the work area. Section 5 will list any known or anticipated hazardous products of combustion. For example, carbon disulfide, when burned, produces toxic gases and irritants, including carbon monoxide and sulfur oxides.

When there is a fire, and time is scarce, it's imperative to know the best way to safely and quickly extinguish the fire. Some burning materials react with water and may best be smothered with foam, carbon dioxide gas, or a dry chemical. Reactivity hazards that enhance the fire, as well as the explosion potential, should also be known. For example, strong oxidizers ignite combustible materials, such as wood, paper, or oil.

Section 6. Accidental Release Measures

Information In This Section. Section 6 provides spill, leak, and response procedures for emergency responders and environmental professionals. It describes evacuation procedures, containment and cleanup techniques, and other emergency advice to protect the health and safety of the responders as well as the environment.

Now I know how the Wicked Witch of the West felt.

Why This Information Is Important. Knowledge presented in Section 6 enables preplanning for emergency response, staff training, and placing necessary equipment in the work area to quickly contain and clean up a spill or leak. Proper containment and cleanup techniques minimize the adverse effects that can occur from an accidental release.

Proper cleanup procedures for flammable materials include the use of nonsparking tools, equipment, and noncombustible absorbent materials and complete decontamination techniques after cleanup to remove any flammable residues.

Section 7. Handling and Storage

Information In This Section. Section 7 provides safe handling and storage information for employees, occupational health and safety professionals, and employers. General handling precautions and practices are described to prevent release to the environment and overexposure during contact with the material, and also to minimize continued contact after handling. For example, *practice good personal hygiene after using this material, especially before eating, drinking, smoking, using the toilet, or applying cosmetics.* Section 7 also explains necessary storage conditions to avoid damage to containers, contact with incompatible materials and subsequent dangerous reactions, evaporation or decomposition of the stored material, or flammable and explosive atmospheres in the storage area. For example, *protect these containers from physical damage, shield them from direct sunlight, and maintain their temperature at less than 38 °C (100 °F).*

Why This Information Is Important. Stored containers cannot be assumed to be safe. Containers corrode, and lids leak. Sparks or heat can cause fires or explosions. Storing incompatible materials close together can cause dangerous reactions. Knowing how to safely handle materials and prevent unsafe storage conditions protects workers from potential hazards.

It ain't much, but I call it home.

Section 8. Exposure Controls/Personal Protection

Information In This Section. Section 8 discusses methods intended for occupational health and safety professionals and employers for reducing worker exposure to hazardous materials. Exposure controls include engineering controls such as ventilation and special process conditions (e.g. isolation, enclosure), or administrative controls (e.g. training, labeling, warning devices). Section 8 also provides guidance on personal protective equipment (PPE) including respirators, safety glasses, goggles, gloves, aprons, and boots. PPE recommendations are given for anticipated normal use and emergency response during a fire, spill, leak, or accidental release.

Somebody should tell this guy his fly is open.

If established, exposure limits or guidelines, such as OSHA PELs or ACGIH TLVs, may be listed in Section 2 or Section 8. (See Section 2 for a detailed explanation.)

Why This Information Is Important. When a job responsibility includes working directly with a hazardous material, this section of the MSDS explains what controls should be in place. If the MSDS states that exposure should not exceed a certain level (i.e. OSHA PEL) or gloves are needed to prevent skin absorption, the employer should provide the necessary controls (e.g. ventilation) and PPE to ensure safe working conditions. However, it is the employee's responsibility to use the PPE that is provided.

To reduce exposure, engineering controls in the workplace are superior to administrative controls, which are superior to personal protective equipment. Sometimes a combination is necessary to reduce overall exposure. A trained professional, such as an industrial hygienist or a safety engineer, should determine how to most effectively minimize hazards through exposure controls.

Section 9. Physical and Chemical Properties

Information In This Section. Section 9 lists physical data, including a material's boiling point, solubility in water, viscosity, specific gravity, melting point, evaporation rate, molecular weight, etc., and appearance and odor. They can help predict how the material will act and react so safe handling procedures can be determined and appropriate personal protective equipment can be selected.

Uh-oh, I'm really tipping the scales. No more twinkies for me.

Why This Information Is Important. Safe handling and use is ensured when it is known ahead of time how a material will behave at different temperatures or when it is exposed to water, etc. For example, calcium metal reacts with water to generate highly flammable hydrogen gas.

If a material has a low boiling point, high vapor pressure, and a high percent volatility, it will evaporate rapidly and is very likely to be an inhalation hazard. Special ventilation or breathing apparatus may be necessary. If the material is also flammable or toxic, even stronger precautions will be necessary. In general, the higher the temperature, the more active the material, i.e. the faster it evaporates, reacts, etc.

Section 10. Stability and Reactivity

Information In This Section. There are many different ways that materials may react with one another. The information presented in Section 10 should list materials and circumstances that could be hazardous when combined with the material covered by the MSDS. This section provides information on chemical incompatibilities, conditions to avoid, decomposition products, and the material's stability.

If I had arms, I'd really do a number on this clown.

Why This Information Is Important. A material can be stored and handled more safely when it is known how it may react to changes in temperature or contact with other materials. This section tells if the material will polymerize (react with itself), a phenomenon that can cause a rapid buildup of heat and pressure that can lead to an explosion. The information in this section helps in making the choice of materials for containers, shelving, and PPE. For example, if the material reacts with metal, it should be stored on non-metal shelves. If the material reacts with natural rubber, a respirator or gloves made of natural rubber should not be worn, and a rubber stopper should not be used to close the bottle.

Some materials may react with common materials, or may burn, or spontaneously decompose to yield by-products that are more toxic than the starting materials themselves. For example, otherwise harmless plastic sheeting can form a deadly gas when burned, and mixing bleach (sodium hypochlorite) with ammonia gives off highly toxic and irritating chloramine.

Section 11. Toxicological Information

Information In This Section. Section 11 provides information on toxicity testing of the material and/or its components. Generally, the information reflects animal testing, although some human data will be available if accidental human poisonings have occurred and the exposure amounts are known, or if epidemiological studies have been conducted. The information in this section is intended for medical professionals, occupational health and safety professionals, and toxicologists.

Data types include acute, subchronic, and chronic studies through various routes of exposure: inhalation, ingestion, skin, eye, intraperitoneal, etc. A typical example of data found in this section is *Rat, Oral, LD_{50}: 200 mg/kg* which means that 200 milligrams of the chemical per each kilogram of body weight is the lethal dose that killed 50% of a group of test rats following oral administration. These data are used to help establish the degree of hazard to humans. Data specific to a material's carcinogenicity, teratogenicity, reproductive effects, neurotoxicity, and mutagenicity may also be provided.

Why This Information Is Important. Toxicological data is invaluable in evaluating the potential health risks that a material may pose to exposed workers. Human evidence of health effects in exposed populations is often not available for the majority of chemicals used or produced in the workplace. Therefore, professionals must rely on toxicological animal data in order to predict the health effects that might occur in humans.

Section 12. Ecological Information

Information In This Section. Section 12 helps in evaluating the effect a chemical may have if it's released to the environment. It may also be useful in evaluating waste treatment practices. Ecotoxicity data may include information on acute and long-term toxicity to fish and invertebrates, or plant and microorganism toxicity. Chemical behavior in the air, soil, or water is important data when evaluating environmental contamination. Such information could include persistence and degradation, soil mobility, bioaccumulation, and photolytic stability.

You sure meet some strange characters in this business.

Why This Information Is Important. Ecological information can be crucial in the event of a major spill, or when determining whether or not a chemical can be safely disposed of in a landfill. If a chemical is rapidly mobile in soil, then it is not a good candidate for landfill disposal because it could potentially leach into groundwater. If a spill occurs in water, knowing ecotoxicity data and the material's behavior in water (i.e. solubility, degradation) can help determine if the spill poses a threat to fish and the best cleanup approach to avoid further environmental contamination.

Section 13. Disposal Considerations

Information in This Section. Section 13 provides proper disposal information for environmental professionals or individuals responsible for waste management activities. Information may include special disposal methods or limitations per

Federal, state, or local regulations, and waste management options, such as recycling or reclamation. It may also include RCRA waste classifications and EPA waste identification numbers and descriptions.

Why This Information Is Important. Section 13 will assist in determining the proper disposal methods and thereby, prevent environmental damage, public health hazards, violation of laws and regulations, and hefty fines.

Section 14. Transport Information

Information In This Section. Section 14 provides shipping classification information for the employer, distributor, emergency responders, and transport/shipping departments. If regulated, shipping information includes U.S. Department of Transportation (DOT) hazardous materials description/proper shipping name, hazard class, and identification numbers (UN or NA numbers). Additional DOT information and international regulatory transportation information such as IATA (International Air Transport Association), ADR (European Agreement Concerning the International Carriage of Dangerous Goods by Road), or Transport Canada regulations for shipping dangerous goods, may be included.

Why This Information Is Important. Section 14 will help transport/shipping departments properly prepare materials for shipment and generate the accompanying documentation. Improperly packaged materials could result in a hazardous exposure or dangerous reaction during handling and transport. Knowing the DOT hazard class and identification numbers enables you to recognize the potential hazards associated with a material.

Section 15. Regulatory Information

Information In This Section. Section 15 provides regulatory information for employers and regulatory compliance personnel. U.S. Federal regulations such as OSHA, TSCA, SARA, CERCLA, and CWA are addressed. Reportable quantities (RQ) for spills or discharges and threshold planning quantities (TPQ) for hazardous materials stored at facilities are listed. Section 15 may also include international regulations such as Canada's WHMIS (Workplace Hazardous Materials Information System), Europe's EINECS (European Inventory of Existing Commercial Chemical Substances), Japan's MITI (Chemical Substance Control Law), or Australia's NICAS (National Industrial Chemicals Notification and Assessment Act). International regulatory information is helpful to those exporting materials outside the U.S. Because many states have specialized requirements in addition to the OSHA *Hazard Communication* standard, Section 15 may also list specific state right-to-know laws.

Just doing some light bedtime reading.

Why This Information is Important. Section 15 will help in complying with the various Federal, state, and international regulatory requirements.

Section 16. Other Information

Information In This Section. Section 16 provides a location for additional information, such as a list of references, keys/legends, or preparation and revisic indicators. Hazard ratings defining the acute health, flammability, and reactivity hazards of a material may also be included.

Why This Information Is Important. Section 16 allows flexibility for additional information and ensures a complete MSDS. Hazard rating systems in this section provide a simple, recognizable, and easily understood reference to evaluate a material's hazards.

Turn to Quiz on page 139.

VI. First Aid

Laboratory accidents don't happen often, but when they do, they're sometimes followed by panic, chaos, and a rude awakening by both the injured person and his or her classmates or co-workers. Why wait until an accident occurs to step up the awareness of the potential dangers of working with hazardous materials? Don't make it easy for a hazardous material to hurt you. We enjoy the challenge.

While a classroom situation may not reach the proportions of an industrial incident, the steps used to control the situation are the same. I have both caused and witnessed enough laboratory and industrial accidents to know the proper course of action. I'll let you in on the steps you should take in case of an accident involving a hazardous material. Come on, we've got a lot of ground to cover.

Step 1: Pause to assess the situation. Don't rush in.

Emergency situations tend to make you act before you think. For instance, when you were young, did you ever play in the sun all day long until you worked up such a thirst that, when your mom called you inside for a cold drink, you rushed so fast that you didn't have time to consider the possibility that the sliding glass door might be closed? Ouch! Nose first, no less. The memory makes me cringe.

Well, this kind of leap-before-you-look reaction is also a big mistake when dealing with any accident in your lab. Don't rush in to help; you'll only risk becoming another victim. For example, if a classmate located four stations behind you is overcome by fumes generated during an experiment, and you run over to help without first assessing the situation, you'll both be contaminated. From the moment the incident occurs to the moment it's resolved, you must first and foremost consider your own safety.

Step 2: Call for help.

If it's simply a matter of getting a band-aid for the small cut your classmate got when picking up the broken pieces of a glass test tube, you can probably handle the situation. However, if the test tube contained an acid that splattered on your classmate when it broke, notify your lab instructor immediately. If your lab instructor is not present, first have someone else send for emergency personnel while you concentrate on making sure the acid is washed off and keeping your injured classmate calm. Acids can cause serious burns, so the sooner a trained emergency medical responder is contacted, the better chance your classmate ha of avoiding serious injury.

When calling or sending someone for help, always provide specific details. Thi crucial information should include what kind of chemical is involved, as well a description of the victim's status (conscious, unconscious, degree of pain). Mal sure that the person informed understands how serious a particular situation is and that you need trained help (medical personnel, fire fighters, etc.). Simply asking for "more help" could send a battery of untrained people to the rescue, making the situation even worse.

Step 3: Pay close attention to the situation.

While waiting for help to arrive, continue to pay close attention to the situation Monitor your own physical condition to determine if the accident has affected your health. Before you assist in cleanup or touch the victim, you must first put on the appropriate protective equipment (gloves, goggles, etc.) to prevent beco ing injured yourself.

Learn the basics

You are not *expected* or *required* to provide medical treatment to an injured classmate or fight a lab fire. Your lab instructor would normally call all the sho but it doesn't hurt for you to know this information also. What if it was your lat instructor that was injured? Knowledge of a few simple first aid and safety rule could make the difference between no injury at all and a serious, even permane injury. Here are some things to remember:

a. Acids are very corrosive substances. Even an acid as dilute as vinegar can irritate the skin if allowed to remain on it for an extended time. Vinegar or lemon juice splashed in the eye will certainly cause some pain. A concentrated acid, such as hydrochloric acid, will cause even more pain. Bases, such as sodium hydroxide, leave a slippery feeling on the skin. Wearing safety glasses or a face shield and gloves should prevent this contact, but accidents do happen. Make sure that the acid or base is washed off your classmate's skin or out of their eyes immediately. It is very important to note the exact location of eyewash stations and safety showers in your lab so you can get to them quickly in case of an accident. (Whenever I travel by plane, I always locate the nearest exit in case of an emergency. Don't you?) If an eyewash station is not available, place your injured classmate on their back, turn their head so water can't run from the contaminated eye to the uncontaminated eye. Gently pour clean water so that it lands on the brow and runs into the contaminated eye. Continue to rinse the eye for at least 15 minutes.

Neutralizing a base with an acid or an acid with a base is acceptable for adjusting the pH of solutions in class, but it is not recommended for exposures to skin, eyes, or accidental ingestion. The vigor of reaction and heat that can be generated during neutralization outweigh any potential benefit. Stick with water.

b. Solvents, such as toluene, acetone, and chloroform produce sweet-smelling vapors. If you or a classmate are working under a fume hood and you smell the vapors or feel light-headed, pull down the hood door all the way and breathe in some fresh air. Chances are the air-velocity or pull in the hood isn't high enough, or something is broken. Tell your instructor immediately. Never continue working if you smell the solvent or become light-headed.

c. If your classmate accidentally ingests a chemical, your first reaction might be to induce vomiting. (I hope you're not eating your lunch while you read this.) While it's understandable that you want to help get rid of the material, especially if it's causing pain, vomiting could make matters worse. For example, if a corrosive material is ingested, vomiting may corrode the throat and esophagus even more. In this case, it's best to give large amounts of water to dilute the material. If the material is a solvent, such as acetone or gasoline, vomiting may cause the person to aspirate (draw foreign material into the lungs through the respiratory tract), resulting in choking, severe lung irritation, or possible chemical pneumonia. That's pretty serious stuff.

Always consult medical personnel before you try to induce vomiting. If your classmate spontaneously vomits, position their head below their hips to avoid aspiration. If the person is unconscious, turn their head to the side to avoid choking or aspirating. This may not be the most pleasant situation to deal with, but it could help save your classmate or co-worker from further injury.

d. In a college lab, you are more likely to have a small chemical spill than a fire, but you should know what to do if a fire does break out. In some cases, a fire may be small enough to be doused with water; other times it may be necessary to grab a fire extinguisher. (You should know where the closest one is located, and how to use it.) Be careful! Discharging a fire extinguisher onto a lab table may worsen the situation by scattering and breaking glassware containing chemicals.

A fire inside a small container can usually be extinguished by covering the container with something that won't readily burn. This will smother the fire. Never pick up the container with your hands because it will be H-O-T, and you could severely burn your hands or fingers.

Unfortunately, not all fires are that simple. If a classmate's clothing catch on fire, immediately guide them to a safety shower and drench them with water. If a safety shower is not available, wrap a fire blanket or coat around t victim and roll them on the floor. Douse burned clothing with water to cool it. Make sure medical personnel are called immediately.

Another dangerous situation is an explosion and subsequent fire, such as that caused by pressure bu up in a flask of a boiling flammable liquid, which throw large amounts of noxious smoke and vapors into the air. A large area can quick become engulfed in flames. In this case, out immediately. In the short time it may take to grab a fire extinguisher, you could already be choking on the smo and fumes. If you've ever burned a piece of toast, you know that by the time you unplug the toaster and throw awa the charred portion of your breakfast, the r is already filled with the amount of smoke normally thrown off at a barbecue. That is exactly what can happen; a small amount of smoke can very quickly beco a dense fog. Fire-fighting should be left to the trained experts. Your only responsibility is to get out of the lab *quickly* and call for help. Your school has a procedure in place in case a fire breaks out in your lab. Learn it!

e. Never attempt to physically touch a person who is in contact with a live electrical current. Disconnect the power first, otherwise the rescuer will als need to be rescued.

Turn to Quiz on page 141.

VII. Spill, Leak, and Disposal Procedures

A few years back, I spent some time in a freshman lab. (There was a cute little beaker of concentrated nitric acid I had my eye on.) One day, just as I was dozing off inside my cozy 250 mL flask - CRASH! - I hit the bottom of a sink. I was dazed at first, but it only took me a few seconds to realize that this was a perfect opportunity. A few whiffs of me and those students would be scrambling for the quickest way out. I caught a glimpse of that sassy nitric acid winkin' at me from across the room, and I knew it was now or never. I spied the drain, still damp with water, and oozed my way toward it. Bull's-eye! I hit the water in the pipes and started to vaporize. The students ran for the door. By the time the safety professionals arrived, I'd completely filled the room. The students weren't allowed back in that day. Finally, some privacy.

A spill is like a field day for hazardous chemicals. We can slide all over the floor to make it slippery, we can vaporize into the air, and we can react with other chemicals. Now that I've turned over a new leaf, I see what kind of serious damage I could have caused if those students hadn't immediately left and called for help (but hey, I was blinded by love at the time). For students like you, a spill can be a potentially dangerous situation if you don't know how to handle it. Here are some simple steps to follow:

1. **Be Prepared**
   Know what hazardous chemicals are present in your lab and in what quantity. Read the MSDSs for these chemicals and review with your lab instructor the response procedures in case of a spill.

2. **Protect Yourself From Injury**
   Never expose yourself to a spill situation unless you're certain that you've selected the proper personal protective clothing and you have the information, tools, and equipment necessary to contain, clean up, and dispose of the material in a safe, legal, and environmentally responsible manner.

3. **Evacuate the Immediate Area**
   Until you are certain the spill is not dangerous to people in the surrounding area, keep others away from it. *Immediately* notify your lab instructor of the

spill. If someone has been injured as the result of a spill, first aid may be necessary.

4. **Identify the Spilled Material**
   If you don't know what the spilled material is, ask your lab instructor, look for container labels, CAS (Chemical Abstracts Service) numbers, markings or any piece of information that can be used to determine the identity. Once the material is identified, the MSDS can be consulted to determine the hazards associated with the spill.

5. **Isolate the Spill From Related Hazards**
   Eliminate the sources of potential hazards. For example, if the spilled material is flammable, extinguish all heat and ignition sources (Bunsen burner, etc.). Keep spilled chemicals from contacting other chemicals in the surrounding area.

6. **Contain the Spill**
   Spill containment procedures serve two important purposes. They prevent the further spread of the spill and help make subsequent cleanup more manageable.

7. **Clean Up the Spill**
   Cleanup should continue until the spill area and the surrounding environment have been returned to the conditions they were in prior to the spill.

8. **Dispose of the Material**
   Dispose of chemicals in a manner that complies with local, state, and Federal regulations. Don't automatically dump chemicals down the drain. Investigate recycling and reclamation. A few chemicals can be disposed of down the drain, but they must be properly destroyed or neutralized so as not to pose a hazard to the environment. Do not attempt to neutralize any chemicals without being directed to do so by your lab instructor.

9. **Clean Yourself Up**
   Follow decontamination procedures for clothing and equipment used during a spill incident. Make sure you thoroughly wash all parts of your body which may have been exposed to the chemicals during the spill incident and subsequent cleanup.

10. **Learn From the Experience**
    Discuss ways to avoid similar spills in the future. Examine ways in which future cleanup operations can be handled more safely and effectively. If you found yourself unprepared to react to any of the situations encountered during the spill, get the information needed to prevent this from happening again.

Turn to Quiz on page 143.

VIII. Personal Protective Equipment

There's nothing more disappointing to a hazardous material than seeing a student wearing personal protective equipment (PPE). There's also nothing funnier. We get such a kick out of how you look all dressed up in your goggles, aprons, and gloves. It's like every day is Halloween. Now don't get all self-conscious. You can't possibly look any sillier than this guy.

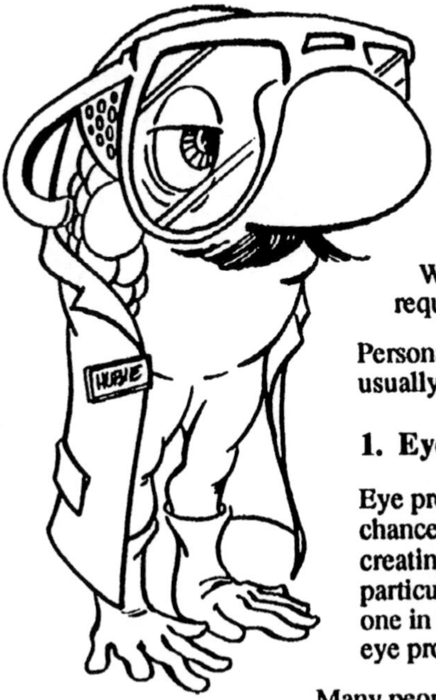

Hey, wait a minute! That's me. Who put that there? Anyway, no matter how hysterical you may look to us, personal protective equipment is an important tool in ensuring your health and safety. Besides, you don't want to end up like our ol' college chum Cheryl, now do you? You've probably got enough bad habits. Why add ignoring protective equipment requirements to the list?

Personal protective equipment in a chemistry lab usually consists of four types:

1. Eye and Face

Eye protection is needed every time there's a chance of spraying or splattering a chemical or creating a dusty situation which could allow particulate matter to enter your eyes. Ouch! Every one in the lab, even visitors, must wear appropriate eye protection *at all times*.

Many people try to avoid wearing safety goggles because they can be uncomfortable, or they've convinced themselves that if they're really, really careful, they won't get the chemical in their eye. GET REAL! If your goggles are uncomfortable, try several other pairs until you find a comfortable fit. Just make sure you wear them, because believe me, you'll be even more uncomfortable if you get spit in the eye by one of my rude cousins.

And don't think you can sneak by with regular glasses or those fancy shades where you can see out but no one can see in. (They give me the creeps.) The goggles required in the lab must meet standards for impact resistance, and must provide splash protection, like the ones with the side shields. And if there's a chance of splashing, implosion, or explosion, face shields or free standing shields will be provided.

Oh, and a word to the wise (from the wise) about contact lens use in the lab. Boy, what a controversy this has been. Everybody's been saying something different - they're okay, they're not okay, they are, they're not . . . What a headache!

Finally, I think the experts have come up with a good contact lens rule. Contact lens use in the lab is acceptable and does not create an additional hazard for the wearer. However, you must still wear the appropriate eye protection *in conjunction with* the contact lenses. HA! Thought this was your loophole, huh? Actually this is a pretty good rule because now people who wear contact lenses kinda get the best of both worlds.

2. Clothing

Lab coats and aprons protect you from gross contamination in the event of a spill or splash. They also protect your clothes, which leads me to wonder where the holes in your jeans came from. What? That's the style? Boy am I getting old.

Style is of little importance in the lab. In fact, certain types of clothing are better left outside of the lab. These include high-heeled or open-toed shoes, sandals, and woven shoes; shorts, cutoffs, and miniskirts. In addition, long hair and loose clothing must be constrained. Other no-nos include rings, which we chemicals like to settle under, and other jewelry that can get tangled in equipment or contac electrical sources.

Here are some additional things to remember:

- Your protective clothing should be easily removable and free from rips, tears, or other defects.
- Wear your lab coat or apron only in the lab.
- Never wear or bring lab clothes or other protective equipment into areas where food is consumed.
- Always wash lab clothes separately from personal laundry.

3. Gloves

Gloves also serve as an excellent form of protection from contamination. Holes in your skin aren't trendy, are they? No? Phew! The jeans I can handle, the skin . . . YUK!

I'm sure you know what rubber or latex gloves look like, and you've probably even used them to keep your hands from getting wet when washing dishes (or are you strictly an eat-out-of-the-container kind of person?), or from getting dirty when changing the oil in your car. Unfortunately, many people don't realize that different gloves are needed to protect against different materials.

Latex gloves protect against water, dirt, and microorganisms, but they don't prevent the absorption of many solvents through your skin. Rubber gloves are adequate for protection against many chemicals, but there are several varieties of rubber [i.e. butyl, natural, Neoprene, fluorocarbon (Viton)], each of which protec against different chemicals. There are also gloves made of polyvinyl chloride or polyvinyl alcohol, and if you work with compressed gases which have very low temperatures, you need cryogenically protective gloves to fend off frostbite. Don't worry. Your instructor will provide you with the appropriate gloves for your specific experiment, but it's always nice to be aware of these things. (See, already you know more than Cheryl ever learned.)

Regularly inspect your gloves for tears or pinholes to make sure you're getting the protection you need. If you notice a hole or tear, or if the gloves are dirty, put on new ones promptly. And if your gloves are too big, too small, or otherwise uncomfortable, find a pair that fits. After use, remove gloves before leaving the work area and before handling items such as a phone, notebook, doorknob, etc.

4. Respirators

Did you ever get stuck sitting in class near a container of hydrogen sulfide? I always did. My teachers just loved that alphabetical order system . . . Helium . . . Hubie . . . Hydrogen Sulfide . . . Boy, did he ever stink up the room. I sure would have liked to wear a respirator those days, especially since there was no fume hood in our classroom.

A respirator is designed to protect you from a chemical by trapping or absorbing the chemical, or by providing you with an "outside" source of breathable air - free of the ambient contaminants. Believe me, I've been in a few locker rooms that could have used this breathable air system.

It's unlikely that you'll need a respirator in your initial college lab work, at least while doing experiments that are brief and use only small amounts of chemicals. Instead, you'll rely on proper ventilation (engineering controls) to protect you. However, your school's *Chemical Hygiene Plan* may require a respirator for some experiments in upper level and graduate courses. The bottom line is, if you're told to wear one, do it. I could easily name a dozen destructive little hazardous materials just waiting for you to slip up so they can turn your lungs into Swiss cheese. Don't let them try.

Remember, if you don't use the safety equipment provided for you, you're not only jeopardizing your health, you're also developing poor safety habits that will follow you into your working life. That's right, I said "your working life". That means your job! Of course it won't be a real job - all of those are taken! No, no, not true. Just a little Hubie humor. There's nothing like it.

Turn to Quiz on page 145.

IX. Laboratory Protocol and Techniques

Hey, are you ready for the big game? You suited up? Have you read the play book? What?! You don't know how to play? It's easy, just follow the protocol. What's the protocol?! Oh, boy . . . time out ref . . . delay of game. We need a huddle.

Following lab protocol is just like abiding by the rules in any organized sport. The biggest difference is that if you bend or break the rules in the big game - foul the shooter, trip the goalie, sack the quarterback after the whistle - the penalty could cost you the game, but it's a small price to pay. In the lab, the rules are not made to keep things fair, but to keep you safe. Break 'em, and the penalty could be infinitely worse, like a serious injury.

Here's the basics of lab protocol. Before you read them, take a minute to think about what it would take to stay safe in the lab. I bet you'll find some of your ideas listed below. After all, safety is mostly a matter of common sense. Let's see how much you have . . .

The Four G's of Lab Protocol

1. General

- Keep drawers and doors closed while working. Bumping and stumbling is a bad idea when you're carrying glassware filled with chemicals.
- Keep the aisles free of chairs, boxes, and those 2-ton book bags you lug from class to class.
- Make sure the floor is clean and dry, and never place apparatus, equipment, or chemical bottles, or your jackets, winter coats, or book bags on the floor.
- Keep your work surface free of anything not needed for the experiment you are performing. When setting up apparatus, give yourself as much space as possible.

And while we're talking neat and clean, let's not forget about personal hygiene:

- Never store or consume food in the laboratory. I love salami on rye as much as the next guy, but I don't think you'd want to share a sandwich with me.

- Never smoke in the lab. Not only is it dangerous, but contaminants can be absorbed by exposed tobacco products. Then when you light a cigarette later, you not only inhale nicotine, you may also get a dose of other toxic chemicals.

- Don't wear or apply makeup in the lab - it may absorb or react with chemicals - and besides, I hear the natural look is in.

- Don't wear jewelry in the lab. Chemicals can seep in and become trapped under rings, and jewelry can get caught on equipment or come in contact with electrical sources.

2. Glassware

Glass is pretty neat stuff - it's inert, easy to clean, inexpensive to make, and can be made into all kinds of cool shapes. The problem is, it breaks easier than a potassium dichromate's heart. (Pretty poetic, huh?) When you break a glass full of your favorite beverage, you can wind up with quite a mess on your hands. When the glass is full of a solution of sodium hydroxide, you've got an even bigger mess, and you better hope it's not on your hands!

When handling glassware:

- Make sure the glassware you use is clean and free from defects - cracks, chips, etc.

- Don't clutter your work area by piling up dirty or clean glassware. It will inevitably lead to breakage.

- Wear protective gloves, and dispose of broken glass properly. Broken glassware is especially dangerous in the lab. If you get cut with glass from a contaminated beaker, the contaminant can enter your bloodstream.

When washing glassware:

- Clean all glassware at the lab sink or in the lab dishwasher.

- Make sure you use rubber mats in your sink and on your work surface to help minimize breakage.

- Wash glassware with hot water and soap or detergent, and always wear gloves.

- Never wash glassware with cleaning agents such as chromic acid or perchloric acid.

When working with glass tubing and rubber stoppers:

- The ends of all glass tubing and rods should be fire polished before use. Handling unpolished glass tubing is like playing with a razor. Not only can it shred your skin, it can also ruin stoppers and rubber hoses.

- When cutting glass tubing, first place the tubing on a firm surface and make a sharp cut with a triangular file, using a quick, firm stroke.
- Always wrap the glass tubing in a cloth before attempting to break it at the cut. If the tubing doesn't easily break, the nick or cut is probably too shallow. Try again.
- When inserting a glass tube through the hole in a rubber stopper, take these extra precautions:

  - Make sure the diameter of the tube is compatible with the size of the hole in the stopper (or flexible hose).
  - Make sure the glass tube has been fire polished (and allowed to cool) before inserting it.
  - Lubricating the glass tube will make things easier. Use water or glycerin.
  - Do not use a rubber stopper if it is cracked, cut, or if the hole is elongated.
  - Hold the glass tubing no more than one inch above the stopper.
  - Insert the glass tube by rotating back and forth with some forward pressure.
  - Hold the stopper so that your hand is not behind the opening on the back side.
- When boring a hole in a new stopper, keep your hand away from the back of the stopper where the boring tool will emerge.

3. Disposal

Okay, so disposal doesn't start with a G, but who's paying attention, anyway? I guess I could have called this section **"Get Rid Of"**, but the Feds don't like that term too much. Anyway, your instructor will provide you with detailed instructions on the proper way to dispose of regulated wastes. My job is just to give you some helpful hints. Your job is to follow them:

- Properly dispose of waste material after each experiment. Don't let beakers filled with used chemicals pile up.
- Keep each different class of chemicals in separate, specifically labeled and dated disposal containers.
- Never pour chemicals into a sink or drain without permission, and then

only if they have been properly neutralized.

- Follow specific instructions regarding any highly reactive materials, such as peroxides, or materials that pose unique hazards, such as biomedical materials, flammable materials, and heavy metals.

- Don't create greater disposal problems by spreading contaminants to sanitary/household waste, such as towels, garbage containers, papers, etc.

4. Gear

My favorite lab gizmo is the centrifuge - what a ride! But there's also some less exciting but no less important equipment, like refrigerators, fume hoods, etc. No matter what you might be using, be familiar with it, know how it works, and how to use it safely. Here are some basic guidelines to remember when using the different pieces of equipment in your lab:

Fume Hood

- Always make sure the fume hood is operating properly before you use it. It is designed to keep contaminants away from your breathing zone. Fume hoods are professionally checked a few times each year, but there's also a quick test you can do. Hold a kimwipe or other light paper towel horizontally in the hood to see if it stands up vertically. Take this little test result seriously, because if the hood is not ventilating properly, you may end up with an unhealthy snootful of my undesirable relatives.

- Hoods should always be used when conducting an experiment that could result in an explosion or implosion (i.e., when using a vacuum pump) or an experiment that could evolve hazardous gases.

Lasers

Talk about intense heat! Lasers are pretty cool, but they can also be pretty dangerous. And because there are so many types and intensities, specific information on any laser used in your lab will be provided to you. However, here are some safety tips:

- Never get near the laser unless you're wearing eye protection designed for the wavelength of the laser used. Remember, no one set of goggles protects against all laser wavelengths.

- Never look directly at the source of the beam.

- Never aim the laser by sighting along the beam.

- Never allow any reflective materials near the beam. This not only includes those cool reflective shades you've been sportin', but also jewelry, and even the shiny buttons on your clothes.

- Always hang warning signs when lasers are in use.
- Make sure the area is well lit to keep your eyes from dilating, which can make it easy for an errant laser beam to "deep fry" your retinas.

Ultraviolet (UV) Lamps

I'll be with you in a minute. I'm working on my tan. Sorry pal, these lamps are perfect for my tough exterior, but they're pretty dangerous for you students. The UV lamps used in your lab have wavelengths of 250 nm or shorter. Not only is this a radiation hazard, but these things can really cook, so remember:

- Always wear UV-absorbing eyewear.
- Use an enclosed radiation box, if available.
- Wear protective clothing if skin exposure is possible.
- Be especially careful with mercury arc lamps. Never touch them with your bare hands. Not only are they very hot, but oil from your skin will leach onto them, causing hot spots, which can lead to early lamp failure.

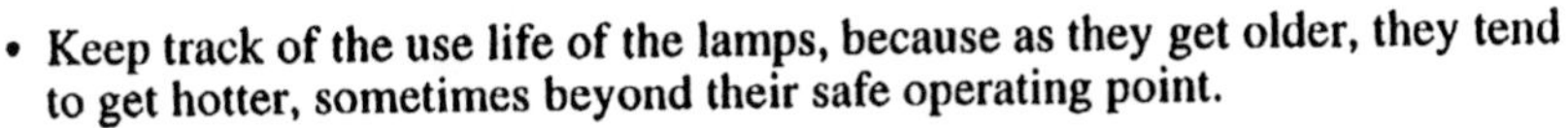

- Keep track of the use life of the lamps, because as they get older, they tend to get hotter, sometimes beyond their safe operating point.

Compressed Gases

These cylinders can be an instant source of major aggravation. (And so can you, according to some of your teachers!) Not only can they store hazardous materials, they do so under pressure; as high as 5000 psi (pounds per square inch).

- Make sure all cylinders are suitably restrained before using them. Even empty cylinders can be dangerous because some of them are very heavy.
- Never heat a cylinder. This not only weakens the metal, it may cause the pressurization relief mechanism to blow, or it may even cause the whole cylinder to rupture. Can you say "grenade"?!
- Never direct high pressure gases at anyone. If you think lasers are dangerous, consider what damage 5000 psi could do if it hit you.
- The threads on the outlets of gas cylinders differ depending upon what is in them. Make sure you use the correct regulator, etc., that corresponds with those threads.

- Never use a cylinder if the identity of its contents is in doubt.
- Always wear safety glasses when working with gases under pressure.

Vacuum Desiccator

I speak from experience when I say that getting dehydrated is no fun. Once it took me three weeks before I got rid of the "raisin look" it caused. So if you don't want to end up with premature wrinkles, remember the following:

- Make sure atmospheric pressure is restored before attempting to open the desiccator.
- Any shielding used must be in place when operating the unit.
- If using a motorized vacuum pump, make sure that all safeguards, such as belt guards, trays, etc., are in place.
- Vent the pump into an exhaust hood, if possible.

Centrifuges

Hey, you didn't think I'd forget about my favorite molecular merry-go-round, did you? Here's a few safety tips you shouldn't forget:

- Make sure the lid is on and secured before operating the centrifuge.
- Make sure the centrifuge is vibration-free up to its full operating speed. If you are not filling the entire centrifuge rack, position your test tubes opposite one another. If you have an odd number of samples, use an empty test tube with an equal amount of weight. (Varying amounts of water are often used.) Never operate an unbalanced centrifuge.
- Keep the rotors and keepers (buckets) clean.

Refrigerator

Everything in the lab refrigerator must be labeled, dated, and double sealed. Speaking of refrigerators, I'm getting hungry. Care to join me? Hold on, there. You didn't pull that sandwich out of the lab refrigerator, did you? These refrigerators should only be used to store hazardous materials, and although that liverwurst smells like it could qualify, it doesn't! Never keep food in a lab refrigerator, and never take any chemicals home and put them into your refrigerator.

X-rays, Generators, and Particle Accelerators

Oh, and speaking of X-rays, generators, and particle accelerators (Were we talking about this stuff?), keep in mind that there are regulations regarding these fancy gizmos. From the NRC (Nuclear Regulatory Commission) on down, strict rules apply (with good reason) when dealing with radioactivity.

Extractions/Distillation Processes

Extractions and distillation processes create a veritable jungle of glass and gear with the potential for trouble (kinda like your weekends). Here are some basic tips to help you:

- When using flammable gases or liquids, remove all burners or other possible ignition sources.
- Keep a pan under your apparatus or experiment in case of a spill. Containment is the key to preventing the spread of any experiment gone awry.

Extractions

Extractions separate substances by taking advantage of differences in solubility of a substance in the different solvents. Extractions can become dangerous when volatile solvents are used. And using glass separating funnels can get tricky because the stoppers can be forcibly ejected, resulting in a spill. Or pressure build-up may even cause the vessel to burst. Take the following precautionary steps:

- Do not attempt extractions until the solution is below or cooler than the boiling point of the extracting solvent.
- When volatile solvents are used, the funnel (without the stopper) should first be swirled. This allows the solvent to vaporize and displace the air in the funnel.
- Close the funnel and invert it while holding the stopper in place. Open the stopcock to release additional vapor and air. Never vent the separating funnel near an open flame or ignition source unless you are planning on becoming the next Olympic Torch!
- Make sure you've got your hand on the barrel of the funnel to keep the stopcock firmly seated. Remember, glass stopcocks should be lubricated; Teflon stopcocks should not.
- Close the stopcock, shake the funnel once with a swirl, and then immediately reopen the stopcock to vent additional vapor.
- If the extraction requires the use of volatile solvents and a separating funnel bigger than liter size, consider performing the extraction in several smaller batches.

Distillations

Whether distillations are done under atmospheric pressure, with an inert atmosphere, vacuum (reduced pressure), or with the addition of steam, make sure the distillation system is designed for safe operation:

- Make sure it's leak-tight to prevent fires or contamination of the work area.

- Never distill to dryness any organic compound suspected of producing peroxides; they become explosive.
- Place a thermometer in the bottom center of the distillation flask, when possible, to monitor for dangerous exothermic decomposition.
- Never go above the temperature prescribed for a given procedure.
- Remember, stirring the distillation mixture is the best way to avoid sudden rapid over-boiling (bumping).
- If you can't stir, use fresh boiling stones. Make sure you put them in before you heat the mixture.

Bumping is more of a problem when distilling at reduced pressures:

- Make sure the heat is evenly distributed.
- Evacuate the assembly slowly to minimize the possibility of bumping.
- Use a standing shield to guard against an implosion.
- Make sure the system has cooled before introducing air, or you may risk an explosion.
- Consider using nitrogen. It's preferable to air and can be used even before the process is cooled.
- Minimize the accumulation of condensation in the distillation flask to prevent overfilling. Using a trap and/or insulating or heating the flask will help.

Temperature Control

Some of the best experiments you'll perform in the lab involve heat. If you heat something too quickly, or if it gets too hot and you don't make provisions to cool it down, you may find yourself up the creek without a paddle - and the creek might be on fire:

- To maintain even, steady heat, use an electric mantle heater or ceramic cavity heater, if possible. Even steam coils or hot water can be used when applicable.
- When using an oil or sand bath as a means of heating, care must be taken to prevent spilling water or any other liquid into the bath. It will cause instant spattering.

- Make sure your experiment/apparatus is designed so that heating/cooling processes can be applied or removed quickly and safely.
- When heating a test tube, never heat from the bottom, but always along the side near the top of the liquid (and use a holder).
- When using hot oil, make sure you know what type of oil is being used and have a method for cooling and storing it.
- Never leave operating baths unattended unless they are properly labeled and a thermostatically controlled shut-off mechanism is being used.
- Viscous liquids transfer heat poorly and require special precautions.
- The rate of most reactions increases as the temperature rises, so reactions can quickly reach violent proportions if you don't allow for adequate cooling methods.

Cooling Methods

Some reactions can be allowed to simply cool down under ambient conditions. However, you should be aware of different cooling methods, because they're required in some processes and often needed in others. Sometimes ice water is all you need. Other times it's not cool enough. To get even lower temperatures, dry ice in combination with an organic liquid is effective, but you can't use just any liquid. The ideal liquid must be: nontoxic; low freezing point; low viscosity - thin enough to readily radiate cold or absorb heat; non-flammable; and low volatility - if it's highly volatile, it's probably flammable.

It may seem impossible to come up with a liquid that has all five characteristics, and a lot may depend on the temperature requirement of a given reaction or process, but you can get pretty close with liquids such as propylene glycol and isopropyl alcohol. And remember, whether you're adding the liquid to the dry ice or vice versa, do it slowly to avoid boil over.

Now if you need to get really cold .... I'm talkin' "too cool for school" cold, reach for a little liquid nitrogen. But don't play it too cool, 'cause this stuff destroys skin tissue on contact! In fact, it's used to treat some kinds of skin cancer. So make sure you're using the appropriate Dewar flask - and if it's glass, it should be encapsulated (wrapped with many layers of duct tape) to prevent flying pieces in the event of an implosion. In fact, just like heating processes, cooling processes also have some general rules:

- Always wear insulated gloves for super cold materials - this includes dry ice as well as cryogenics.
- Never pour cryogenic coolants onto the edge of the glass Dewar - it may cause it to crack. The same applies to pouring coolants out of a glass Dewar. Use a siphon, or better yet, use a metal Dewar flask and eliminate the problem.

- Cryogenic liquids must be stored in properly vented containers.
- Always wear goggles when chipping dry ice.
- When using a vacuum pump in reduced pressure operations, always put a cold trap between the apparatus and the pump to prevent volatiles or other contaminants from being sucked through the pump and out into the atmosphere.
- Be aware that super coolants will rapidly condense oxygen, which may lead to an explosion with combustible materials.
- Always use coolants in a well-ventilated area or under a fume hood. Dry ice and some cryogenic liquids will displace oxygen, which can lead to asphyxiation.

That's it! That's the lab protocol game plan. (Did you forget we still have a game to play?) The most important thing to remember is to follow the instructions given to you. Don't make your own rules, or break the ones already made. The "big game" in the lab is even bigger than the Super Bowl or the World Series . . . it's the game of life - one strike and you're out. (A sappy, yet sincere message from yours truly . . . and the Feds.)

Turn to Quiz on page 147.

X. OSHA Regulations

As one of the world's most famous hazardous materials, I owe a lot of my popularity to the Federal government and to OSHA. OSHA was established by the United States Department of Labor as the government agency responsible for the safety and health of employees in the workplace. The law, known as the *Occupational Safety and Health (OSH) Act* of 1970, became effective April 28, 1971. However, it wasn't until 1985, when the *Hazard Communication* standard came into effect, that people finally took an interest in who I was and what I was all about. In 1988, my popularity once again surged, thanks to those people in Washington. You see, until 1988, the *Hazard Communication* standard applied only to workers in manufacturing jobs. OSHA recommended to Congress that the scope of the standard be extended to workers in other industries who also used hazardous materials on their jobs. When Congress approved this expansion, millions of additional people, including construction workers, health care employees, utility workers, and transportation workers, became big fans of mine.

Since I owe my notoriety (not to mention endorsement deals with a sneaker *and* a soft drink company) to the *Hazard Communication* standard, I thought I'd return the favor by explaining how the standard affects you.

OSHA has jurisdiction over safety and health in all private-sector establishments where there are employees. This includes non-public schools at all education levels. For public-sector establishments, most states have agencies that enforce OSHA standards or adopt their own, sometimes more restrictive safety and health standards. This includes schools funded by public money at all education levels.

OSHA does not consider students in college labs to be employees. (Too bad. Wouldn't it be nice to get paid to come to lab?) If you're performing lab-related activities as an employee of the college, you're covered under the OSHA standards. However, even if you're not considered an employee, you're still responsible for proper handling of hazardous chemicals.

In the hierarchy of hazardous materials management, the highest official on you campus bears the ultimate responsibility for the safety of the staff and students i the school and for meeting the requirements of the OSHA standard that are in effect for your locality. This responsibility is delegated, through other administr tors, to the faculty and students. Without your cooperation, the school cannot operate within the law. All the laws, equipment, procedures, and controls in the world won't protect the person who refuses to act responsibly with and around hazardous materials. Treat safety as part of your lab experience and, when required, use the resources provided by your school. (The Feds made me say all that.)

There are more than 50 OSHA regulations governing health and safety in labora- tories. Unfortunately, I don't have time to discuss them all. (Was that a sigh of relief I just heard from you?) Don't relax yet, because there are a few that shoul be mentioned. Pay attention, because this is important stuff that will help you now and in your future career.

Hazard Communication Standard

The Federal government enacted the *Hazard Communication* standard in response to the dramatic increase in the use of chemicals in the workplace. Many of these chemicals can cause illness and injury if used or handled improperly. The law requires employers to provide their employees with the information and training they need to protect themselves from chemical hazards in the workplace.

Hazard Evaluation

The standard requires employers to figure out what materials in their workplace are hazardous. Many of the materials used on-the-job are purchased from firms who manufacture, distribute, or import chemicals. This law requires these firms to tell employers if these materials are hazardous at the time they're purchased. The law also requires that MSDSs and container labels accompany shipments of all such hazardous materials.

This evaluation stuff can really wear a guy down.

The standard contains a list of chemicals that are considered hazardous. The law also tells manufacturers what guidelines should be used to determine if a material is hazardous.

A workplace may produce its own hazardous materials as products for sale, or as by-products of processes. When this happens, the employer operating the workplace is responsible for developing MSDSs and container labels for these materials.

Hazardous Materials Inventory

Employers must prepare and maintain an inventory itemizing all of the hazardous materials present in their workplace. This list becomes the focus of employers' efforts to obey the standard. The inventory should list each material by the same name used on the MSDS for the material. This inventory is available to employees for review.

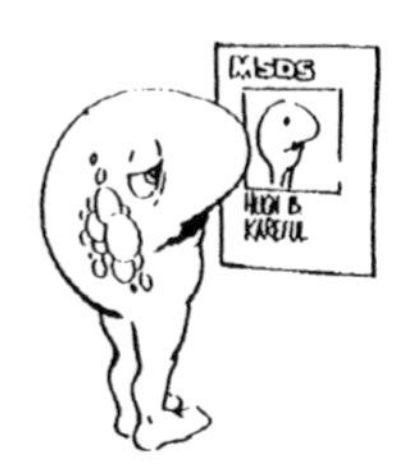

Boy, some of this stuff is pretty personal.

Material Safety Data Sheets

Employers must have an MSDS for each material listed on the hazardous materials inventory. MSDSs are the key ingredients in the hazard communication process. Their purpose is to provide information about hazardous materials. The law requires that all MSDSs be in English. See Section V of this book for more information on MSDSs.

Labeling

Employers must make sure that all containers of hazardous materials are properly labeled. The law helps employers with this requirement by ordering suppliers of hazardous materials to label the containers they use to ship chemicals. OSHA requires that these labels contain the following information:

- Identity of the hazardous material
- Appropriate hazard warnings (specific hazards, target organ effects, precautions, etc.)
- Name and address of the material's manufacturer, supplier, or importer

Hey, you're gonna ruin my view.

If the manufacturer's label falls off or becomes illegible, it must be replaced with a label of equal warning.

Employers are required to label portable containers, tanks, and vessels in their workplace that hold hazardous materials. They can use signs, placards, process sheets, batch tickets, or operating procedures in place of labels, but the format used must include the material's identity and appropriate hazard warnings.

Employee Training

Employers must provide their employees with information and training on the hazardous materials they may be exposed to. Employers must provide this training when new employees are hired, when they are transferred from different job assignments, and when a new hazardous material is introduced into the work area. This information and training will include:

When they come out, they'll know more about me than my mother does.

- An explanation of the standard
- Identification of the hazardous materials, their potential health effects, and where they are located in the plant
- The location and availability of the written hazard communication program and MSDSs
- Procedures to be used to detect and measure workplace contaminants
- Safe work practices and protective equipment employees can use to protect themselves
- An explanation of the labeling system

Trade Secrets

The standard contains guidelines for dealing with trade secrets that give manufacturers some rights to protect proprietary interests. A company's claim that certain MSDS information is a trade secret must be supported by evidence. That company must still provide all of the related properties and hazards of the material and state that specific chemical information is being withheld because it is a trade secret. In the case of emergencies, the standard does provide for manufacturers of these products to release trade secret information upon the request of a treating nurse or physician.

Laboratory Standard

The *Occupational Exposures to Hazardous Chemicals in Laboratories* standard was issued by OSHA in January 1990. For lab employees, this standard supersedes the *Hazard Communication* standard. The scope of the standard is very specific, and its intended objectives differ from the *Hazard Communication* standard. OSHA developed the standard because it recognized that laboratory use of hazardous materials was quite different from industrial use. Laboratories generally use small amounts of many different materials for testing and research purposes.

The *Lab* standard requires employers to maintain employee exposures to hazardous materials at or below acceptable safe levels established by OSHA or another recognized authority (i.e. PELs, TLVs, RELs).

Chemical Hygiene Plan

Employers are free to determine the best way for their laboratories to stay below PELs, etc. OSHA requires each laboratory to develop a *Chemical Hygiene Plan* (*CHP*) that documents the necessary work practices, procedures, and policies intended to keep employee exposure below hazardous levels.

Included are standard operating procedures to follow whenever lab work involves hazardous materials and criteria to determine suspected unsafe exposure levels. The *CHP* must also contain the controls that the employer has in place to protect employees from these unsafe levels, including personal protective clothing, hygiene practices, and special equipment, such as fume hoods and respirators.

Your school has developed a *Chemical Hygiene Plan* for the hazardous materials that you use in the lab. This *CHP* includes the procedures, controls, and equipment your instructor has in place to protect himself or herself, co-workers, and students (like you) from the hazards of the materials you will be using in class. Your instructor will discuss the students' role in the *Chemical Hygiene Plan* with you at the beginning of the semester.

OSHA also wants both employers and workers to be extra cautious when dealing with extremely hazardous substances, such as carcinogens and infectious agents. The standard requires labs to have provisions in place for additional employee protection when work involves extremely dangerous substances. This additional protection should include the establishment of a designated area where all work involving these materials is performed. Employers must make sure that, when needed, containment devices, such as fume hoods and glove boxes, are in use, and procedures for decontamination and safe removal of contaminated waste are in place.

Boy! This lab is ready for all my tricks.

Monitoring Requirements

The standard requires employers to monitor hazardous material levels in the work area if there is "reason to believe" the exposure levels exceed recognized safety limits. If the monitoring shows that an overexposure occurred, employers must act to reduce those levels. Employers must also re-monitor to ensure the problem is corrected.

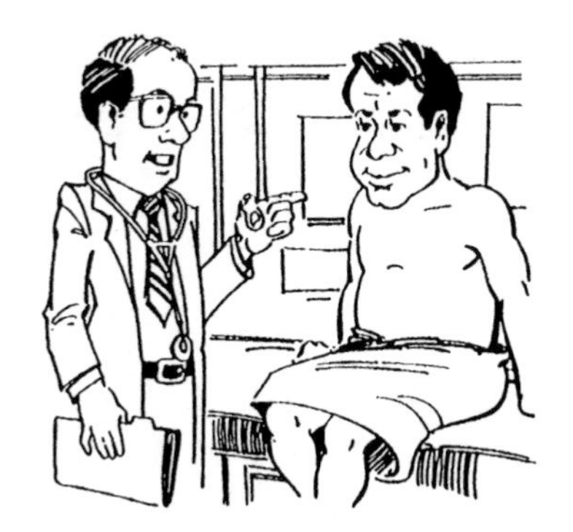

Opportunity for Medical Opinion

Employers must also provide personnel with an opportunity to receive medical attention if evidence suggests that they have been overexposed to a hazardous material in the laboratory. This evidence includes any symptoms of overexposure that may develop, involvement in a hazardous materials accident, or monitoring that reveals routine levels of overexposure in their work area. This medical attention is provided, free of charge, by their employer at a time and place convenient for them. Both the employee and employer are given the complete results of the visit, including any recommendations for follow-up action. Med conditions discovered during this visit that are unrelated to workplace exposu cannot be revealed to their employer.

Employee Training and Information

OSHA, and laboratories in general, recognize that the best way to protect workers from the dangers of hazardous materials is to teach them to protect themselves. The *Lab* standard requires employee training.

Employers must provide workers with the OSHA-established PELs for materials they currently work with. If a material has no PEL, but is considered hazardous by another recognized authority, employers will make their personnel aware of the established exposure limit for the material.

Employees will learn the signs and symptoms typically associated with overexposure to hazardous materials. Employers will also make workers aware of the physical and health hazards caused by overexposure. The standard also requires employers t train all lab personnel in the methods and observations that are used to detect th presence or release of hazardous materials in their workplace.

Much of the training focuses on the laboratory's *CHP*. OSHA requires that lab employees be made aware of its location and that they learn how to use it. Employers are required to review with workers the specific procedures include in the *CHP* to protect them from exposure. These include appropriate work practices, personal protective equipment, and emergency procedures.

In addition, employers are required to maintain MSDSs on each hazardous material in their laboratories. As part of employee training, workers will be informed of the location and availability of these MSDSs along with additional known reference material on the hazards and safe handling, storage, and dispos of materials found in the lab.

OSHA requires employers to provide all employees with this training, both at t time of their initial assignment, and again prior to reassignments involving new exposure situations. OSHA also requires refresher training at the employers' discretion.

Hazard Identification

Employers must ensure that all incoming containers of hazardous materials are labeled properly and that the label is not removed or defaced. If missing or destroyed, a label must be replaced. The MSDSs from the suppliers must be maintained and made available to all employees.

Many labs produce their own materials for use in their operations. In this case, employers must determine if the materials are hazardous. If a material is a by-product of a lab operation, and its ingredients and composition are unknown, the employer must assume that it's hazardous and incorporate it in the *CHP*.

Recordkeeping

Employers must establish and maintain records of any monitoring activities and medical examinations involving each employee during their time of employment and for 30 years after.

Common Sense

Informing everyone of the hazards of working with chemicals and other hazardous materials, how to avoid them, and how to proceed in the event of an accident, makes a lot of sense. Although you are not working as an employee, you still need to learn about safety and develop good habits for lab work. When that glorious day of graduation rolls around and you're about to begin your first day on the job, remember what you've learned here.

HAZWOPER Standard

There's another OSHA law that specifically protects employees who are expected to deal with hazardous wastes they encounter on-the-job. It's called the *Hazardous Waste Operators and Emergency Response* standard, a.k.a. *HAZWOPER*.

I take exception to the term "waste.

Much of the *HAZWOPER* standard addresses large-scale hazardous waste handling and disposal operations like the waste treatment plants where many of my dear departed relatives have been buried. (And not one of them left me anything in their will, the bums!) But schools like yours are affected by *HAZWOPER* too.

Many colleges and universities provide *HAZWOPER* training to members of their maintenance, custodial, or campus security staff to qualify them to respond to emergency and cleanup situations involving hazardous materials that can easily occur on campus. Improperly discarded chemicals, underground storage tank leaks, storage area spills, or on-campus accidents that involve a release of a hazardous substance are all situations where only employees who have met the *HAZWOPER* training requirements can respond.

Generally, in classroom labs, accidents involving hazardous materials are no
significant enough to require *HAZWOPER*-trained personnel to respond. If,
however, you ever encounter a situation where a large amount of a hazardou
material has been accidentally released or you suspect that an exposed mater
particularly dangerous, regardless of how small the amount, don't try to deal
the problem yourself. Report it to your instructor immediately. If necessary,
proper authorities will be contacted.

Bloodborne Pathogens Standard

Blood, products containing blood, live viruses (like my cousin Cyrus the Vir
and bacteria are not technically considered "hazardous chemicals", but they a
also regulated by OSHA. The *Occupational Exposure to Bloodborne Pathog*
standard mandates use of appropriate protective clothing and equipment in o
to prevent exposure to bloodborne pathogens such as the Hepatitis B Virus
(HBV) and the Human Immunodeficiency Virus (HIV).

Avoid contact with the blood or body fluids of another person in the lab. If an
emergency situation exists and you come to the aid of a bleeding classmate or
instructor, make sure you are wearing adequate protection, including rubber
gloves and goggles. Never attempt to pick up broken glass, needles, or other
sharp objects that have punctured someone else's skin without using tools and
waste containers that will prevent further punctures to yourself and others.

Turn to Quiz on page 149.

XI. What's So Important About the EPA and Environmental Data?

Hazardous materials like myself are constantly being generated and used. We love to be spewed into the air, dumped into the landfills, and spilled into the waters. These are a few of our favorite things. My sisters, the dioxide twins (nitrogen and sulfur), create quite a stir when they hit the air. They're very sociable, mingling with dust and water molecules to form smog and acid rain. But you humans don't enjoy smog and acid rain like we do. They make it difficult for you to breathe, they pollute the air, and they kill plants and animals. What fun! Oh, sorry. I reverted back to my dastardly ways for a second.

Anyway, that's why the Environmental Protection Agency (EPA) was established in 1970. They're like the chaperones at a high school dance. If it wasn't for them, we'd be "spiking" the rivers with toxins, and sneaking off to the bathroom to "light up" some combustibles. The EPA's primary responsibility is to keep hazardous materials under control by administering programs that address environmental problems such as toxic substances, air and water pollution, industrial waste disposal, solid waste management, pesticides, radiation, and noise. The EPA is concerned with the safe manufacture, use, and transportation of hazardous chemicals. The agency often requires manufacturers to conduct tests on materials or products which may pose a hazard to public health and safety or the environment. The EPA also establishes automotive emission standards.

The Good Ol' Days?

My grandfather often reminisces about the Industrial Revolution. It was the hazardous materials' hay-day. There were no restrictions. People were dumping chemicals and toxic wastes like there was no tomorrow. (Kind of a sad pun, huh?) I guess they thought it would all safely disappear into the world's vast skies and waters. People were caught up in the whirlwind of new, fast-producing machines. How many of them stopped to think about the consequences? Not enough, I guess.

For years following the Industrial Revolution, dirty, smoke-filled air plagued many cities, and fishing became impossible in what used to be plentiful waters. My grandfather fondly recalls these "happier" days. Then, like the human equivalent of Black Monday, the hazardous materials experienced their own Great Depression. Rumors flew through the family grapevine . . . there was talk of establishing rules and limits for handling and *disposing* of hazardous material to fight the growing environmental problems. Aaagh!! My ancestors were running scared.

Many industries fought against it. Products containing chemicals had become seemingly indispensable. People could no longer imagine having to wash their laundry by hand, read by candlelight, or ride a horse to get everywhere. The industry leaders believed that pollution control was far too costly, and would only result in driving up the cost of their products. The hazardous materials secretly cheered them on, but a compromise was finally made.

Clean Air Act

In 1955, the first attempt at controlling pollution was passed by Congress. The original *Clean Air Act* (CAA) was aimed at controlling unspecified particles from being spit into the air by factories, but the regulations were too vague to be followed uniformly across the country. In 1970, 1977, and 1990, major revisions helped establish what is now a list of 190 hazardous air pollutants. Lots of my relatives are on this list. They're very proud.

The CAA is different from other Federal acts because it's directed toward by-products discharged into the air from stationary sources (i.e. factories) and mobile sources (i.e. automobiles and airplanes), rather than the use and assessment of specific chemicals. Emissions considered capable of changing the ambient quality of air are regulated by the EPA through a system of national emission limits and permits.

Talk about alphabet soup! These letters and acronyms can drive you nuts!

Clean Water Act

The *Clean Water Act* (CWA) was enacted in 1972. It's a complete revision of the unsuccessful *Refuse Act* of 1899 that failed to control expanding and continuing water pollution. Pollution had become so bad that many rivers turned orange and green. And in 1969, a river in Ohio actually caught fire!

The CWA's ultimate goal is to eliminate all discharges of hazardous materials into the U.S. waterways. It also strives to make all U.S. waterways safe for fishing and swimming. The Act is designed to regulate the discharge of toxic and non-toxic pollutants (oil, heat, toxic waste, bacteria, etc.) into waterways by municipal and industrial sources. Under the CWA, these sources must obtain a National Pollutant Discharge Elimination System (NPDES) permit from state officials or the EPA. This permit specifies types of control equipment and discharge limits for the specific facility based on the amount of pollution the receiving body of water can handle. The CWA also provides for civil penalties, up to $250,000, for illegal discharge of a substance into the environment, and makes the discharger responsible for cleanup costs. Its success can be measured by the growing number of waterways now suitable for fishing that were polluted 20 years ago.

Resource Conservation and Recovery Act

In 1976, Congress passed the *Resource Conservation and Recovery Act* (RCRA). It actually began ten years earlier with the *Solid Waste Disposal Act*. Unfortunately, the newly created EPA was busy with the CAA and CWA, so enforcement of the RCRA law was difficult. RCRA concentrates on the recycling and disposal of hazardous wastes. It divides hazardous wastes into 6 categories according to their hazardous characteristics, and assigns them one or more of the following codes: ignitable waste (I); corrosive waste (C); reactive waste (R); toxicity characteristic waste (E); acute hazardous waste (H); and toxic waste (T). RCRA regulates the activities of all parties involved in the generation, transport, storage, or disposal of these wastes. These parties must comply with a number of notification and recordkeeping requirements that enable the material to be tracked for 30 years.

Comprehensive Environmental Response, Compensation, and Liability Act

The *Comprehensive Environmental Response, Compensation, and Liability Act* (CERCLA), also known as "Superfund", was established in 1980 to close the final loophole in environmental regulation - identifying and fining those responsible for hazardous waste spills. The law gives the EPA authority to collect cleanup costs from the responsible parties and to establish a fund when the responsible parties can't be identified (i.e, abandoned dump site), or won't or can't pay. If the responsible party does not voluntarily provide cleanup, the fund is used to issue the needed money so cleanup can begin, and those involved are taken to court for reimbursement. This fund is extremely important; without it, many dangerous hazardous waste spills or leaks would continue to contaminate the air, water, and soil until the court cases are settled. Imagine how long that could take! In fact, before this fund was created, some of my greasier relatives were dumped into a river. They sat there for *two years* just waiting to be rescued. They were so bored. I mean, you can only contaminate so many fish.

Superfund Amendments and Reauthorization Act

Finally, the *Superfund Amendments and Reauthorization Act* (SARA) of 1986 was enacted to help local and state agencies respond to spills. It requires the use of inventory reports that show amounts and storage locations of chemicals on a site. It also provides citizens and local governments with information about potential hazards in their community.

Phew! We made it. These regulations can get pretty complicated, but they all have one common goal - to protect you and the environment from becoming victims of the hazardous materials in industry. (We get such a bad rap.) The EPA regulations certainly keep us hazardous materials from having fun, but they keep you and the environment healthy, and that's what really matters (to you, anyway).

The Times . . . They Are A Changing (Woa, Woa, WOE)

The times are changing for all of us. These laws are no longer the only restrictions faced by businesses that use chemicals to make products or deliver services. The public's growing environmental awareness is a much stronger force. More and more consumers are choosing to do business with companies that operate in an environmentally responsible manner. This means more people are buying hamburgers at fast food restaurants that use paper wrappings instead of styrofoam; are making their lawns greener with organic nutrients instead of chemical fertilizers; and are buying more and more products that either can be or have been recycled.

Woe is me and chemicals like me. Our days of unrestricted use and fun are well over. I don't think we'll ever live in a world without chemicals, but if people do business with companies committed to protecting the environment, well, let's just say that your kids will have a more promising future than my kids will. By the way, this message comes from me, Hugh B. Kareful, not the Feds. (I do have a sensitive side.)

Know Thy Chemistry

Can you be counted among those that are experiencing this environmental awareness? If so, then I probably don't have to tell you how important your knowledge of chemicals is to your cause. What's that? You want to hear it anyway? Great!

For starters, it's no longer a matter of just learning to concoct something in class. It's equally critical to know what happens to that concoction when you're finished with it. You can't just dump it down the drain. What chemicals would you be dumping? Where would they go? What damage could they do?

There are many chemicals that can destroy the pipes in your sink; in fact, trichlorosilane feasts on metal. (You should see him at the dinner table!) And sodium metal reacts with water to generate highly flammable hydrogen gases. (Remember my little vaporizing trick in the lab? I never did get close to that little concentrated nitric acid. Turns out she'd really been winkin' at the sulfuric acid on the table behind me.) If your school has a leach field or a break in an underground pipe, many of us could get in the groundwater and create a problem. Some hazardous materials can even survive the municipal waste water treatment plant, and may end up in the river where you swim or fish.

So What's the Big Deal?

Hey, my ride to the airport is here. Talk about traveling in style! On the way, I think we should have a little heart-to-heart. See, we may not have started out on the right foot, me being a convicted felon and all, but I think we've both learned a few things. However, you may still be wondering why you need to know all this stuff; why someone like me, the Feds, and your instructor would go through all this trouble to make sure you learn to protect yourself. I wondered the same thing myself at first. But now that I've really had a chance to think about all this information, the answer is pretty obvious - to help you lead a longer, more productive and healthy life. Still doubtful?

Let's go over it quickly. I've given you lots of reasons why working safely with chemicals is so important. I've also told you about the laws that were established to protect you. I've given you all kinds of helpful hints and valuable information that you can use again and again, like how to read an MSDS, how to handle a lab emergency, how the chemicals you use can harm you and how to safely work with them, how to recognize hazard warnings, why exposure limits are so important to your health and safety, and how to safely dispose of hazardous materials. And that's not all! I haven't even given you my helpful tips for working safely with chemicals, or that wonderful list of chemical profiles yet. Wow, no wonder I'm so tired!

But suppose, even after all my hard work, you think to yourself, "I won't get injured working with these chemicals. That only happens to other people." Oooh, that really burns me up! I bet Cheryl said something like that, and look where it got her. In fact, the number of students and workers who get hurt each year by improperly using chemicals is pretty steep. I'm not just talking about a few dozen accidents. Heck, I've been involved in that many in one month. I'm talking about *thousands* of injuries a year. People losing their eyesight, scarring their faces, permanently damaging their lungs, even dying because they weren't careful when working with hazardous materials. This means that it *could* happen to you. My mission is to convince you that taking chemicals for granted is a big mistake. All it takes is one second of carelessness with a hazardous chemical to damage your life forever. Why take the chance?

Okay, so maybe I've finally convinced you that you need to protect yourself when working with hazardous chemicals, but you don't think it matters what happens to a chemical when you're finished with it. Suppose you say, "I'm just one person. It's no big deal if *I* don't follow all those rules and regulations, as long as everyone else does." You might think that the small amounts of chemicals you use in class couldn't possibly be enough to cause a problem. Oh, where did we go wrong with you? Stop a minute and think about this: What if *every* student around the country dumped *everything* they used in four years of lab classes down the drain? It doesn't make for a pretty picture (although Grandpa would disagree).

Schools like yours are being put under more pressure and scrutiny as they scramble to comply with *all* of the regulations, not just the ones I explained. Scores of colleges are being fined *hundreds of thousands of dollars* for improperly storing and disposing of hazardous chemicals used or produced on their campuses. In fact, the cost for managing and disposing of hazardous chemicals is now a major line item in the budget of most schools.

Every administrator, teacher, and student must share the responsibility for complying with government regulations. Failure to comply could cause major problems, and your school could face some of those heavy-duty fines. And here's the real kicker - you may think that it's the school that suffers the consequences, but who really pays the price when, because of these fines, your school announces fewer class selections, bigger classes with fewer instructors, and an increased tuition rate?

Turn to Quiz on page 151.

XII. Tips for Working Safely with Chemicals

Now you know *most* of the secrets of my hazardous materials family. You didn't expect me to tell you everything, did you? Some things are just too secret to reveal, like the fact that it was really Ol' Uncle Cadmium that caused the explosion at the Bromine family wedding last month. Oops, I let that one slip pretty easily. Well, you're not getting the details out of me, that's for sure. After all, I'm a respected leader among my peers. What would they think if I started spilling information like that?

What's that? What do you mean my family and friends are calling me Hubie "backstabbing, double-crossing, big mouth fink" Kareful? I'll show them. I've still got a few tricks up my sleeve. Before leaving for the airport, I put together this list of basic safety tips for you to follow whenever you're in the lab, as a student now and a professional later on.

Lab Safety Tips

1. **Think Safety First**
   Plan your work and include safety as part of your plan. Use your mind as a crystal ball and visualize the potential hazards you need to be protected against. Then make sure you prepare yourself and your work area with whatever is necessary to protect you from these hazards.

2. **Know Emergency Responses**
   Know the location of emergency phone numbers, first aid supplies, appropriate fire extinguishers, eyewash stations, showers, etc. In most cases, the quicker you react to a hazardous chemical exposure, the less damage will result.

3. **Know What You're Working With**
   Be familiar with the chemicals you work with. Review the MSDSs and container labels and test your knowledge often. You should know how the material could hurt you or others, under what conditions it can hurt you, how to avoid these conditions in your lab, and should these conditions occur, what you must do to safely and effectively respond to the situation.

4. **Follow All Safety Procedures**
   Always follow the rules and procedures established by the head of your laboratory. If you're not supposed to perform a task by yourself, don't. If

you're supposed to wear goggles at all times, wear them. Handle regulated wastes exactly the way you've been taught. Don't ignore warning signs and placards; read them carefully and respond accordingly. People just like you have been seriously hurt and even killed in laboratories just like yours because they were in a hurry or took safety for granted.

5. **Report Dangerous Activities or Situations**
   A container missing a label or two incompatible materials dangerously positioned near each other are examples of real-life lab situations that can cause serious physical and environmental damage. If you see or sense something wrong in your lab, tell your lab instructor immediately. Don't ever expect someone else to do something about a hazard you discover. Get it corrected NOW!

6. **Store and Handle Hazardous Materials Safely**
   Practice good housekeeping and personal hygiene. Store chemicals safely and transport them as directed by lab policy and the suppliers' directions. If a container label falls off, make sure it is replaced. Make sure all contaminated clothing and equipment is properly decontaminated. If a chemical spills or leaks through a container, get it safely cleaned up as soon as possible. Wash your hands after handling any chemical or chemical container, even if you were wearing gloves while handling the chemicals. Never eat or drink in areas where hazardous chemicals are used or stored.

7. **If You Don't Know . . . ASK!**
   If you have a question about a hazardous chemical, ask your lab instructor. If you think you're experiencing symptoms of overexposure to a hazardous chemical, report them immediately.

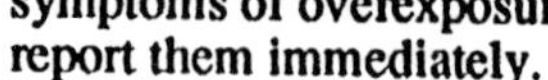

XIII. Chemical Profiles

Thought you'd seen the last of me, didn't ya? Well, now they've got me holed up in this airport waiting room with the rest of the hazardous materials. I can't take off until I fork over the chemical profiles I promised you. I guess this is your lucky day. Not only will I give you more than 90 first-rate profiles, but you also have the dubious honor of witnessing the last time I'll ever have to sit on one of these storeroom shelves. What a drag it can be! Once I got stuck over a holiday weekend next to a container of iodine. All he did was stare at himself in the mirror and admire his violet-black coloring. He was so annoying! I knew he was fishing for a compliment, so I commented on his sharp, characteristic, irritating odor. I guess that's not what he wanted to hear!

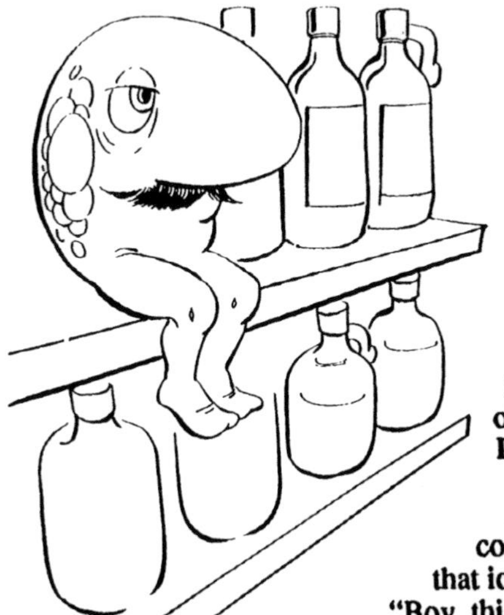

Anyway, we're nearly finished here, but before I change into my floral swim trunks and rub coconut oil on my legs (don't ask me how), I'll pass along the profiles on many of the chemicals that you might encounter during your college lab courses. (And if you ever come across that iodine, make sure you loudly exclaim, "Boy, this stuff stinks!")

Turn to these profiles before every lab to get a run-down on the potential hazards of the chemicals that you'll be working with on that particular day. The information includes a brief description of the chemicals; what their hazards are (if any), i.e. flammable, reactive, corrosive, toxic; their basic health effects; and their incompatibilities. At the end of each summary is the statement: "Listed (or not listed) as a RCRA Hazardous Waste". If it is listed, one or more of four words will follow: "Corrosivity"; "Ignitability"; "Reactivity"; or "Toxicity". These words tell you what property of the material has caused its regulation under RCRA. For example, if a material is listed as ignitable, it will have a flash point less than 60 °C (140 °F). If it's corrosive, it may have a pH less than 2 or greater than 12.5. If a material is listed as reactive, it may react violently with water (exothermically), generate toxic vapors, gas, or fumes when mixed with water, or be readily capable of detonation or explosive decomposition at standard temperature and pressure. If a material is listed as toxic, it is itself or contains a material that is considered to pose a human health threat when released in certain quantities.

These are only some examples; for a detailed list of criteria on characterizing a hazardous chemical, see (40 CFR Part 261.20 to 261.24). If you don't find a profile for a particular material, ask your instructor to provide the information.

The diamond-shaped symbol next to each profile is known as the fire diamond. It is a hazard rating system for materials developed by the National Fire Protection Association (NFPA). On page 102 of the glossary, you'll find a complete explanation of how the fire diamond system works. To borrow a line from a popular song (feel free to hum along), "Fire diamonds are a chemical user's best friend." Turn to page 102 to find out why.

Acetic Acid, Glacial [CH_3COOH] A clear, colorless, mobile liquid with a sharp, pungent, vinegar-like odor. Acetic acid, glacial is highly corrosive and can cause severe skin and eye burns. It is a combustible liquid and may react with alkaline and oxidizing materials. Listed as a RCRA Hazardous Waste, Ignitability.

Acetone [CH_3COCH_3] A colorless, highly volatile liquid with a sweetish odor. High vapor concentrations may produce narcosis (unconsciousness). Prolonged or repeated skin contact causes dryness, irritation, and mild dermatitis. Acetone is a dangerous fire and explosion hazard. Listed as a RCRA Hazardous Waste, Ignitability.

Alizarine Yellow R [$C_{13}H_9N_3O_5$] An odorless, yellow-brown powder, orange-brown needles from dilute glacial acetic acid. Direct skin and eye contact may be irritating. A potential for allergic contact dermatitis exists for recurrent exposures. *Not* listed as a RCRA Hazardous Waste.

Aluminum Hydroxide [$Al(OH)_3$] A solid, white, bulky, amorphous powder; odorless. Aluminum hydroxide exhibits rather low toxicity by ingestion and inhalation; it can be found in some antacid preparations. Direct eye contact may produce irritation and eye burns are possible depending upon the duration of contact. *Not* listed as a RCRA Hazardous Waste.

Aluminum Metallic Powder [Al] Gray to silver powdered metal. It is a respiratory and eye irritant. Powdered aluminum can be a severe fire and explosion hazard. Aluminum reacts with strong acids and alkalis to release flammable hydrogen gas. It also reacts with oxidizing materials, acid chlorides, and metal salts. Listed as a RCRA Hazardous Waste, Reactivity.

Ammonia, Aqueous [$NH_3(aq)$] Colorless liquid with a strong, suffocating odor. Aqueous ammonia liquid and vapor is immediately and extremely irritating and corrosive to the eyes, skin, and respiratory tract. Aqueous ammonia solution is not combustible, but the vapor is. Listed as a RCRA Hazardous Waste, Corrosivity.

Ammonium Acetate [CH_3COONH_4] White deliquescent (readily moisture-absorbing) crystals with a slight vinegar odor. Ammonium acetate dust is mildly irritating to the skin, eyes, mucous membranes, and respiratory tract. It is moderately toxic by ingestion. Ammonium acetate is combustible, but does not ignite easily. *Not* listed as a RCRA Hazardous Waste.

Ammonium Chloride [NH_4Cl] Colorless crystals or white granular powder; odorless. Ammonium chloride is mildly irritating to the skin, eyes, mucous membranes, and respiratory tract. If decomposed in a fire, highly irritating fumes of hydrochloric acid and ammonia can be released. *Not* listed as a RCRA Hazardous Waste.

Fire

Nonfire

Ammonium Dichromate [$(NH_4)_2Cr_2O_7$] Orange-to-red crystals or needles; odorless. Ammonium dichromate is a skin and respiratory irritant. It may cause ulcers of the nasal passages and pulmonary edema (fluid in the lungs). It is a strong oxidizing agent that may explode on contact with organic materials. Listed as a RCRA Hazardous Waste, Toxicity, Ignitability.

Ammonium Nitrate [NH_4NO_3] Colorless, crystalline solid; odorless. Ammonium nitrate is irritating to the eyes, skin, nose, throat, and mucous membranes. If decomposed in a fire, highly toxic oxides of nitrogen gases are emitted. It is a strong oxidizing agent that reacts with strong alkalis (to liberate ammonia), reducing agents, strong acids, powdered metals, and organic materials. Listed as a RCRA Hazardous Waste, Ignitability.

Barium Chloride [$BaCl_2$] Colorless crystals or white powder; odorless. Barium chloride may cause irritation of the eyes, nose, throat, and bronchial tubes. It is highly toxic by ingestion. Listed as a RCRA Hazardous Waste, Toxicity.

Barium Sulfate [$BaSO_4$] A white or yellowish powder; odorless. Barium sulfate is relatively nontoxic to humans due to its extreme insolubility in water. It is not combustible and is very stable and relatively inert. Heating barium sulfate and aluminum together can cause an explosion. *Not* listed as a RCRA Hazardous Waste.

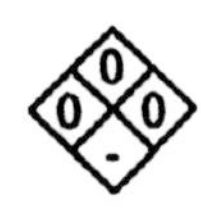

Bromine [Br_2] A dark, reddish-brown, noncombustible diatomic liquid. Bromine is an extremely toxic chemical and its solutions are corrosive to all body tissue. Inhalation of bromine vapor is severely irritating to the respiratory tract and may lead to lung damage. Bromine is a strong oxidizing agent that reacts vigorously with reducing agents, combustibles, and many organic chemicals. Contact with water produces toxic and corrosive fumes. Listed as a RCRA Hazardous Waste, Reactivity.

Calcium Carbonate [$CaCO_3$] White powder or colorless crystals; odorless. Classified as a nuisance dust and may be irritating to skin, eyes, and respiratory tract. Calcium carbonate is incompatible with acids; alum; ammonium salts; and (mercury + hydrogen). It ignites on contact with fluorine. *Not* listed as a RCRA Hazardous Waste.

Calcium Chloride [$CaCl_2$] White, deliquescent crystals, flakes, granules, or lumps with no odor. Calcium chloride can be very irritating to the skin, eyes, and mucous membranes. Concentrated solutions may cause skin ulcerations and burns. Contact with water produces an exothermic (heat-producing) reaction. *Not* listed as a RCRA Hazardous Waste.

Calcium Hydroxide [$Ca(OH)_2$] Colorless, hexagonal crystals or soft white granules; odorless. Calcium hydroxide is a skin, mucous membrane, and respiratory tract irritant, and a severe eye irritant. Contact with eyes can cause severe eye burns. Not listed as a RCRA Hazardous Waste.

Carbon Dioxide [CO_2] Colorless gas; clear, colorless, volatile liquid; or a white solid; odorless. Carbon dioxide is relatively inert, but it can cause asphyxiation by displacing oxygen. Contact with liquid or solid CO_2 (dry ice) can produce frostbite and freeze burns. Dusts of manganese, aluminum, and chromium ignite and then explode when heated in CO_2. Other incompatibles include acrylaldehyde, aziridine, metal acetylides, and sodium peroxide. *Not* listed as a RCRA Hazardous Waste.

Chlorine [Cl_2] A greenish, yellow gas with a pungent, suffocating, nauseating odor. Chlorine is a highly toxic and corrosive gas and is very irritating to eyes and mucous membranes. Although it is non-combustible, it is a strong oxidizer that supports the combustion of other organic materials. It is an extremely reactive and explosive gas. It reacts with many common substances such as acetylene, ammonia, hydrogen, ether, fuel gas, hydrocarbons, turpentine, and finely divided metals. Listed as a RCRA Hazardous Waste, Reactivity, Ignitability.

Copper [Cu] Red/brown metal or powder; odorless. It may be toxic through contact, inhalation, and ingestion. In general, animal studies suggest that copper compounds have the potential to cause damage to the liver, kidneys, spleen, and blood. Copper may cause skin and eye irritation and a flu-like syndrome called metal fume fever. Handling copper may cause skin discoloration. It is not considered a fire hazard, but fine particles may burn in air. Copper reacts violently with ammonium nitrate, bromates, iodates, chlorates, hydrogen peroxide, sodium peroxide, sulfuric acid, and sodium azide. *Not* listed as a RCRA Hazardous Waste.

Copper (II) Nitrate Trihydrate [$Cu(NO_3)_2 \cdot 3H_2O$] Blue deliquescent crystals or powder; odorless. It is irritating to the skin, eyes, and respiratory tract. It is moderately toxic by ingestion. Copper (II) nitrate trihydrate is an oxidizer and can react violently, possibly causing fire and/or explosion, with organic matter (paper, wood, etc.), combustible materials, and reducing agents. Listed as a RCRA Hazardous Waste, Ignitability.

Copper (II) Oxide [CuO] Also called cupric oxide. Black crystalline powder; odorless. Inhalation of copper oxide dust and fumes may cause metal fume fever and irritation of the mucous membranes of the nose and upper respiratory tract. Eye and skin contact with dust particles can cause irritation. Copper (II) oxide can react vigorously with hydrazine. Violent reactions may occur on heating with aluminum, boron, magnesium, potassium, sodium, titanium, and zirconium. *Not* listed as a RCRA Hazardous Waste.

Copper (II) Sulfate [$CuSO_4$] Grayish to greenish-white crystals or crystalline granules or powder; odorless. Copper (II) sulfate is acidic when dissolved in water. Contact with the skin and eyes is irritating. Ingestion can cause nausea, vomiting, diarrhea, gastritis (inflammation of the mucous membranes of the stomach), damage to the kidney tubules, and hemolysis (disruption of the red blood cells). It reacts violently with magnesium and hydroxylamine. *Not* listed as a RCRA Hazardous Waste.

Copper (II) Sulfide [CuS] Blue-to-black hexagonal crystals or powder. Copper (II) sulfide is moderately toxic by inhalation and ingestion. It is combustible. It explodes on contact with magnesium chlorate, zinc chlorate, cadmium chlorate, or concentrated chloric acid solutions; and may react violently with hydrogen peroxide or (ammonium magnesium nitrate + water). Contact with moist air causes copper (II) sulfide to oxidize to copper sulfate. *Not* listed as a RCRA Hazardous Waste.

Cyclohexane **[C_6H_{12}]** Colorless, volatile mobile liquid with a sweet odor; pungent when impure. Cyclohexane is a dangerous fire hazard. It is irritating to the eyes, skin, and mucous membranes and may cause central nervous system depression at high concentrations. Listed as a RCRA Hazardous Waste, Ignitability.

Ethanol, Ethyl Alcohol **[CH_3CH_2OH]** Clear, colorless, very mobile, fragrant liquid with a burning taste. Ethanol is an eye and mucous membrane irritant and central nervous system (CNS) depressant. Avoid exposure to high vapor concentrations. The IARC lists ethanol as a confirmed human carcinogen for ingestion of beverage alcohol. Chronic ethanol ingestion is associated with hepatoma (liver cancer). It is a dangerous fire and explosion hazard. Listed as a RCRA Hazardous Waste, Ignitability.

Glycerol **[$C_3H_5(OH)_3$]** Colorless or pale yellow syrupy liquid; odorless; sweet taste. Glycerol is a skin and eye irritant and is mildly toxic by ingestion. In the form of a mist, it is an inhalation irritant. It is incompatible with strong oxidizing agents, alkali metal hydrides, acetic anhydride, calcium oxychloride, and chromium oxides. *Not* listed as a RCRA Hazardous Waste.

Hydrochloric Acid **[HCl(aq)]** A clear, colorless-to-lightly yellowed, fuming liquid; sharp, pungent, characteristic, irritating odor of hydrogen chloride gas. Hydrochloric acid is a corrosive irritant to the skin, eyes, and mucous membranes. This strong mineral acid is very reactive with bases and incompatible with many materials. The corrosive action of hydrochloric acid on most metals can liberate extremely flammable/explosive hydrogen gas. Listed as a RCRA Hazardous Waste, Corrosivity.

Hydrogen Gas **[H_2]** Colorless, tasteless, odorless gas that is much lighter than air. Hydrogen is highly flammable and explosive when exposed to heat, flame, or oxidizers. The gas is relatively inert although it becomes a simple asphyxiant at high concentrations by replacing oxygen. Rapid release of compressed gas or contact with the liquid may cause frostbite. *Not* listed as a RCRA Hazardous Waste.

Hydrogen Peroxide **[H_2O_2]** Colorless liquid with a slightly acrid odor. Hydrogen peroxide is considered low in toxicity at 3% (household use) but classified as corrosive if greater than 8%. It is a strong oxidizer and can cause severe eye, skin, and respiratory tract irritation and burns. Hydrogen peroxide reacts with a wide range of materials and, although noncombustible, it is an oxidizer that can release oxygen to increase combustion of other materials. Listed as a RCRA Hazardous Waste, Ignitability.

Iodine [I_2] Violet-black solid; sharp, characteristic, irritating odor. At room temperature, iodine sublimes to a violet gas. Iodine vapors can severely irritate the respiratory tract, mucous membranes, eyes, and skin. Iodine is a strong oxidizing agent, and as such, it supports combustion vigorously. It is reactive with many other chemicals and should be used with caution. Listed as a RCRA Hazardous Waste, Ignitability.

Iron [Fe] Pure, solid iron is a silvery-white or gray, soft, ductile, malleable metal. It is available as ingots, wire, sheets, or powder. The powder form is black-gray. Iron is moderately toxic by ingestion and inhalation of iron dusts and powder. The powder form is pyrophoric. Powder is listed as a RCRA Hazardous Waste, Reactivity.

Iron (II) Ammonium Sulfate Hexahydrate [$Fe(NH_4)_2(SO_4)_2 \cdot 6H_2O$] Light green deliquescent crystals. Iron (II) ammonium sulfate hexahydrate is an eye, nose, and throat irritant. In large doses, this iron salt is a corrosive and systemic poison. *Not* listed as a RCRA Hazardous Waste.

Iron (III) Chloride [$FeCl_3$] Black-brown solid. Iron (III) chloride solutions are corrosive to the skin, eyes, and mucous membranes. Reacts with water to form toxic and corrosive fumes. Forms shock-sensitive explosive mixtures with some metals (e.g. potassium, sodium). Violent reaction with allyl chloride. Listed as a RCRA Hazardous Waste, Corrosivity.

Iron (III) Nitrate [$Fe(NO_3)_3$] Deliquescent, pale violet or grayish-white crystals. Iron (III) nitrate is irritating to eyes, nose, and throat and is moderately toxic by ingestion. It is combustible and a strong oxidizer that is a dangerous fire hazard in contact with organic material (wood, paper, oil). Iron (III) nitrate is incompatible with aluminum, cyanides, phosphorus, acetylene gas, and reducing materials. Listed as a RCRA Hazardous Waste, Ignitability.

Iron (II) Sulfate Heptahydrate [$FeSO_4 \cdot 7H_2O$] Odorless, blue-green crystals or granules. Contact with dusts or mists is irritating to the eyes, skin, and respiratory tract. It is a reducing agent that is incompatible with alkalis and oxidizing agents. *Not* listed as a RCRA Hazardous Waste.

Lead, Elemental [Pb] Bluish-white, silvery, gray, very soft metal. Inorganic lead is a potent systemic poison that affects a variety of organ systems, including the nervous system, kidneys, reproductive system, blood formation, and gastrointestinal (GI) system. The most significant way lead enters the body is through inhalation, but it can also be ingested when lead dust or unwashed hands contaminate food, drink, or cigarettes. Lead dust is flammable and moderately explosive when exposed to heat or flame. Listed as a RCRA Hazardous Waste, Toxicity.

Lead (II) Nitrate [$Pb(NO_3)_2$] Colorless crystals or white crystalline powder; odorless. Lead (II) nitrate is a powerful oxidizer and can accelerate and intensify combustion of flammable and combustible materials. It is probably a severe eye, skin, and mucous membrane irritant. It is moderately toxic by ingestion. Listed as a RCRA Hazardous Waste, Toxicity, Ignitability.

Lead (II) Sulfate [$PbSO_4$] White, heavy crystalline powder. Lead (II) sulfate is a corrosive irritant to the skin, eyes, and mucous membranes. Its toxicity results primarily from lead. It reacts explosively with potassium. Listed as a RCRA Hazardous Waste, Toxicity.

Litmus Blue, amorphous powder, lumps, or cubes, with a decaying plant odor and often compressed into small cakes or applied to strips of paper. Litmus changes color with acidity of solution, red at pH 4.5 and blue at pH 8.3. Litmus is relatively nonhazardous. *Not* listed as a RCRA Hazardous Waste.

Magnesium Hydroxide [$Mg(OH)_2$] White powder, odorless. Magnesium hydroxide is a skin and mucous membrane irritant. It is incompatible with maleic anhydride and phosphorus. *Not* listed as a RCRA Hazardous Waste.

Magnesium Metal [Mg] Silvery white metal; odorless. Magnesium metal in the form of fine powder, thin sheets, and turnings is easily ignited and burns with intense heat. When moisture is present, magnesium fires flare up violently because it reacts with moisture to produce highly flammable hydrogen. Powders form explosive mixtures in air that can be ignited by a spark. Magnesium metal reacts violently with chlorinated solvents, methanol, hydrogen peroxide, oxidizing agents, sulfur compounds, animal and vegetable oils, metal oxides, metal cyanides, metal oxide salts, oxygen, and tellurium compounds. Inhalation of magnesium dust and fumes can cause metal fume fever. Particles imbedded in the skin can produce sores that resist healing and an accumulation of gas under the skin and gaseous blebs (small blisters). Listed as a RCRA Hazardous Waste, Reactivity.

Magnesium Sulfate, Heptahydrate [$MgSO_4 \cdot 7H_2O$] Colorless crystals or white powder; odorless. It is moderately toxic. Eye contact and prolonged or repeated skin contact may cause irritation. *Not* listed as a RCRA Hazardous Waste.

Manganese (IV) Oxide [MnO_2] Also called manganese dioxide. Lumps appear steel-gray, fine powder is black to brownish-black; odorless. It is a strong oxidizer. Do not heat or rub with oxidizable substance (sulfur, sulfides, phosphides, hypophosphites, etc.) or organic matter. Reacts violently with hydrogen peroxide. Inhalation of manganese dioxide dust can irritate the respiratory tract and lead to an increased incidence of respiratory infection and lung damage. Listed as a RCRA Hazardous Waste, Ignitability.

Manganese (II) Sulfate [$MnSO_4$] Translucent, reddish crystals; odorless. Manganese sulfate normally presents little acute health hazard, except at very high exposure levels. Chronic exposure may cause severe neurologic and behavioral disorders (manganism). Neurologic damage can be permanent if exposure is not recognized early on and continues. Manganese sulfate can cause violent decomposition of hydrogen peroxide (52% by weight or greater). *Not* listed as a RCRA Hazardous Waste.

Mercury [Hg] A silver, heavy, odorless liquid. Mercury is highly toxic by skin contact/absorption or inhalation. It causes respiratory and digestive disturbances and repeated exposure leads to nervous system problems, including memory loss and tremors. It may react with various acids. Listed as a RCRA Hazardous Waste, Toxicity.

Mercury (I) Chloride [Hg_2Cl_2] A white, heavy, odorless powder. Mercury (I) chloride is irritating to the eyes, skin, and respiratory tract. A skin rash may result. Repeated exposure leads to nervous system disturbances. May react with certain salts and alkaline materials. Listed as a RCRA Hazardous Waste, Toxicity.

Methane [CH_4] A colorless, odorless, extremely flammable gas. Added mercaptans give it the characteristic 'rotten egg' smell. Methane is flammable at temperatures as low as -136 °C (-213 °F) and is explosive in air. Toxicity occurs from oxygen displacement in air and results in asphyxiation. Listed as a RCRA Hazardous Waste, Ignitability.

Methanol [CH_3OH] Also called methyl alcohol. A clear, colorless, volatile liquid with a slight alcohol odor when pure and a pungent odor when crude. It is highly flammable and explosive and reacts with metals and oxidants. Methyl alcohol is highly toxic to the

nervous system and can result in blindness. Skin contact can cause dermatitis. Listed as a RCRA Hazardous Waste, Ignitability.

Methyl Orange [$C_{14}H_{14}N_3NaO_3S$] Orange-yellow crystalline scales or powder. It is nonflammable but decomposes into irritating nitrogen and sulfur oxides when heated. Relatively nontoxic but may cause mild eye and skin irritation. *Not* listed as a RCRA Hazardous Waste.

Nickel Sulfate [$NiSO_4 \cdot 6H_2O$] Blue to blue-green, odorless crystals. It is nonflammable but decomposes into toxic nickel carbonyl fumes and sulfur dioxide gas when heated. It is mildly irritating and may cause asthma or dermatitis. *Not* listed as a RCRA Hazardous Waste.

Nitric Acid [HNO_3] A water-white to slightly yellow liquid that darkens on exposure to light and has an acrid, suffocating odor. It is a strong oxidizer and although not flammable, will ignite combustible materials. It reacts with many materials, including metals and alkalis. Nitric acid is very corrosive to human tissue and can produce severe burns of the eyes, skin, and respiratory tract. Listed as a RCRA Hazardous Waste, Corrosivity, Ignitability.

Nitric Oxide [NO] A colorless gas with a sharp, sweet odor. It is nonflammable, but as a strong oxidizer it may ignite combustible materials. Its toxicity is due to its ready oxidation to nitrogen dioxide (NO_2) in air that can cause lung damage. High concentrations cause oxygen depletion and death can result from lack of oxygen. Listed as a RCRA Hazardous Waste, Toxicity, Ignitability.

Nitrogen Dioxide [NO_2] A yellow-brown fuming liquid below 21 °C (70 °F) or a reddish-brown gas above; with a pungent, acrid odor. A strong oxidizer that may cause combustible materials to ignite. The liquid is corrosive to skin; the gas is irritating to the respiratory tract and can cause severe lung damage and tooth erosion. Listed as a RCRA Hazardous Waste, Toxicity, Ignitability.

Oxalic Acid [$(COOH)_2$] A white, crystalline, odorless powder that readily absorbs moisture from air. Combustible when heated, producing toxic formic acid. It is a strong acid and causes irritation and burns of human tissue. Oxalic acid disturbs the body's calcium balance and in turn damages the kidneys. *Not* listed as a RCRA Hazardous Waste.

Phenolphthalein [$C_{20}H_{14}O_4$] White or yellowish, odorless crystals. Incompatible with strong oxidizing materials. Phenolphthalein is relatively nontoxic although ingestion may cause diarrhea. Combustion causes a release of toxic carbon and nitrogen oxides. *Not* listed as a RCRA Hazardous Waste.

Phosphoric Acid [H_3PO_4] A viscous, water-white, odorless liquid. Incompatible with alkalis and corrosive to many metals. It is irritating to skin and may cause burns. Mist inhalation is irritating and corrosive to the respiratory tract. Listed as a RCRA Hazardous Waste, Corrosivity.

Potassium Bromide [KBr] Colorless crystals or white powder with no odor. Eye or skin contact is mildly irritating and prolonged exposure may result in acne-like eruptions. Chronic ingestion can cause central nervous system depression. *Not* listed as a RCRA Hazardous Waste.

Potassium Chloride [KCl] Odorless, white crystals or powder. It is relatively nontoxic although ingestion of large amounts can cause gastrointestinal disturbances. *Not* listed as a RCRA Hazardous Waste.

Potassium Chromate [K_2CrO_4] Odorless, lemon-yellow rhombic crystals. It is a powerful oxidizer and is incompatible with hydrazine and easily oxidized materials. Inhalation or skin/eye contact is highly corrosive and may cause asthma and dermatitis after chronic exposure. Listed as a RCRA Hazardous Waste, Toxicity (as chromium), Ignitability.

Potassium Dichromate [$K_2Cr_2O_7$] Odorless, bright orange or red crystals. A strong oxidizer that ignites combustible materials. It is highly irritating and repeated exposure can cause ulcerations of the skin and nasal septum (tissue between the nostrils). Listed as a RCRA Hazardous Waste, Toxicity (as chromium), Ignitability.

Potassium Hydroxide [KOH] Odorless, white, hygroscopic, crystalline flakes, lumps, or pellets. Releases heat in contact with water and acids and corrodes many metals when wet. It is highly corrosive to all human tissue and may cause permanent injury. *Use extreme caution!* Listed as a RCRA Hazardous Waste, Corrosivity.

Potassium Iodide [KI] Colorless or white granules or powder. Incompatible with acids and alkaline salts. It is slightly irritating to the eyes, skin, and respiratory tract. Chronic exposure may cause Iodism (see glossary). *Not* listed as a RCRA Hazardous Waste.

Potassium Nitrate [KNO_3] Odorless, white, crystalline granules or powder. A strong oxidizer capable of igniting combustible materials. Incompatible with many metals. It is irritating to the eyes and respiratory tract and may cause anemia, kidney damage, and gastro-intestinal disturbances after repeated exposure. Listed as a RCRA Hazardous Waste, Ignitability.

Potassium Permanganate [$KMnO_4$] Odorless, dark purple or bronze crystals. A strong oxidizer which is incompatible with numerous materials and capable of creating explosions. Concentrated solutions and dry crystals are highly corrosive to human tissue. Repeated skin contact can cause dermatitis. Listed as a RCRA Hazardous Waste, Ignitability.

Potassium Sulfate [K_2SO_4] An odorless, creamy white granular powder. Incompatible with active metals such as aluminum and magnesium. It is mildly irritating to the eyes, skin, and respiratory tract. *Not* listed as a RCRA Hazardous Waste.

Potassium Thiocyanate [KCNS] Colorless, odorless, transparent, deliquescent crystals turning brown, green, then blue when fused. Ingestion of large or chronic doses causes mental derangement, collapse, rashes, and disorders of the blood and thyroid. Emits toxic cyanide fumes when heated. *Not* listed as a RCRA Hazardous Waste.

Potassium Triiodide [KI_3] Dark brown, hygroscopic crystals. Causes irritation of the eyes, skin, and respiratory tract. Chronic exposure may result in Iodism. *Not* listed as a RCRA Hazardous Waste.

Propane [C_3H_8] A highly flammable, colorless gas at room temperature and 1 atm pressure. Liquefied by lowering temperature or raising pressure. Incompatible with oxidizers, (barium peroxide + heat), and chlorine dioxide. Irritating to the eyes and respiratory tract. Inhalation of high concentrations results in asphyxiation and/or anesthetic effects. Listed as a RCRA Hazardous Waste, Ignitability.

2-Propanol [$CH_3CHOHCH_3$] Also called isopropyl alcohol (rubbing alcohol). Clear, colorless liquid with a slight, non-residual alcohol-type odor. Isopropyl alcohol is an eye irritant that can cause corneal burns and eye damage. Repeated or prolonged contact with the skin may cause irritation and dermatitis. High concentrations may cause narcosis. It is a dangerous fire hazard and a moderate explosion hazard when exposed to heat, flame, or oxidizers. Some incompatibles cause explosions. Listed as a RCRA Hazardous Waste, Ignitability.

Silver Bromide [AgBr] Pale yellow crystals or powder turning black on exposure to light. Incompatible with potassium and sodium. Irritating to the eyes, skin, and respiratory tract. Chronic exposure may cause a gray pigmentation of the skin and mucous membranes, fatigue, and mental disturbances. Listed as a RCRA Hazardous Waste, Toxicity.

Silver Chloride [AgCl] White, granular powder turning black on exposure to light. Not as irritating as other silver salts because of its low solubility. Chronic exposure may cause argyria, a permanent gray pigmentation of the skin and mucous membranes. Listed as a RCRA Hazardous Waste, Toxicity.

Silver Nitrate [$AgNO_3$] Large, colorless, transparent crystals or small white crystals; odorless. A strong oxidizer that reacts dangerously with many acids and phosphorus derivatives. Toxic silver and nitrogen oxides are emitted when heated. Irritating to eyes, skin, and respiratory tract. Chronic exposure leads to argyria, a permanent gray pigmentation of the skin and mucous membranes. Listed as a RCRA Hazardous Waste, Toxicity, Ignitability.

Sodium Acetate [CH_3COONa] Hygroscopic, colorless to white crystals with a slight vinegar odor. Incompatible with strong oxidizers. Mildly irritating to the eyes, skin, or respiratory tract. Will ignite, but not easily. *Not* listed as a RCRA Hazardous Waste.

Sodium Bromide [NaBr] Hygroscopic, white or colorless crystals or powder. Incompatible with acids, strong oxidizers, and alkaloidal or heavy metal salts. Ingestion of large amounts may cause dizziness, impaired reflexes, and listlessness. Chronic exposure may cause mental disturbances. *Not* listed as a RCRA Hazardous Waste.

Sodium Carbonate [Na_2CO_3] Odorless, white hygroscopic powder. Corrosive to steel when in heated solution. Irritating and corrosive to eyes, skin, and respiratory tract; severity depends on concentration. *Not* listed as a RCRA Hazardous Waste.

Sodium Chloride [NaCl] Colorless, transparent crystals or white, crystalline powder. Incompatible with cement and bromine and corrosive to many metals. Inhalation of high concentrations may cause irritation of the eyes and respiratory tract. *Not* listed as a RCRA Hazardous Waste.

Sodium Chromate [Na_2CrO_4] Odorless, yellow, translucent, efflorescent crystals. A strong oxidizer. Incompatible with combustibles. Irritating and corrosive to the eyes, skin, and respiratory tract.

Chronic exposure may cause liver, blood, or kidney damage. Listed as a RCRA Hazardous Waste, Toxicity, Ignitability.

Sodium Dichromate, Dihydrate [$Na_2Cr_2O_7 \cdot 2H_2O$] Odorless, red-orange crystals or powder. A strong oxidizer that causes combustible materials to ignite. Explodes on contact with acetic anhydride. Irritating and corrosive to the eyes, skin, and respiratory tract. Chronic exposure may cause liver, blood, or kidney damage. Listed as a RCRA Hazardous Waste, Toxicity, Ignitability.

Sodium Hydroxide [NaOH] Odorless, hygroscopic, white flakes, lumps, or pellets. Incompatible with acids and water; generates large amounts of heat. Strong, corrosive alkali that dissolves human tissue. *Use with caution!* Listed as a RCRA Hazardous Waste, Corrosivity.

Sodium Hydroxide, Solution [NaOH(aq)] Odorless, clear liquid. Incompatible with acids; generates large amounts of heat. Strong, corrosive alkali that dissolves human tissue and causes permanent injury. *Use with caution!* Listed as a RCRA Hazardous Waste, Corrosivity.

Sodium Hypochlorite [NaOCl] A white, crystalline solid or clear, pale yellow to green liquid with a chlorine odor. A strong oxidizer capable of igniting combustibles. Reacts violently with amines and soaps. Highly irritating to the eyes, skin, and respiratory tract; severity depends on concentration. Listed as a RCRA Hazardous Waste, Ignitability.

Sodium Iodide [NaI] Odorless, white hygroscopic crystals or powder that slowly turn brown on exposure to air. Incompatible with alkaloidal and metallic salts. Irritating to the eyes, skin, and respiratory tract. Chronic exposure may cause Iodism. *Not* listed as a RCRA Hazardous Waste.

Sodium Nitrate [$NaNO_3$] Odorless, hygroscopic, colorless crystals or white powder. A strong oxidizing agent capable of igniting combustibles. Mildly irritating to the eyes, skin, and respiratory tract. Listed as a RCRA Hazardous Waste, Ignitability.

Sodium Sulfate [Na_2SO_4] Odorless, white, hygroscopic granules or powder. Incompatible with aluminum and magnesium. Irritating to the eyes, skin, and respiratory tract. *Not* listed as a RCRA Hazardous Waste.

Sodium Thiosulfate [$Na_2S_2O_3$] Nearly odorless, white, transparent powder or crystals. Slowly decomposes at room temperature and more rapidly in presence of light or heat. Incompatible with oxidizers. Mildly irritating to the respiratory tract and skin (may cause dermatitis). *Not* listed as a RCRA Hazardous Waste.

Sucrose [$C_{12}H_{22}O_{11}$] Odorless, white crystals, lumps, or powder. Combustible and may explode if ignited when finely divided. Incompatible with nitric or sulfuric acid. Slightly toxic if ingested in large amounts. *Not* listed as a RCRA Hazardous Waste.

Sulfur [S] Yellow crystals or powder. Odorless when pure. Highly reactive with many materials and explosive when heated in finely divided form. Irritating to the eyes and respiratory tract. *Not* listed as a RCRA Hazardous Waste.

Sulfur Dioxide [SO_2] A colorless gas or liquid with a sharp, pungent odor. The liquid corrodes many metals. It forms corrosive sulfuric acid on contact with mucous membranes or moist skin, accounting for much of its toxicity. The lungs can be severely damaged by inhalation. Can trigger asthmatic attacks. *Not* listed as a RCRA Hazardous Waste.

Sulfuric Acid [H_2SO_4] An odorless, colorless (when pure) to dark brown (impure) dense, oily liquid. Reacts violently with water, generating much heat. Incompatible with numerous materials. Extremely corrosive to body tissue resulting in severe burns and possible permanent damage (scarring and blindness). Listed as a RCRA Hazardous Waste, Corrosivity, Reactivity.

Zinc Chloride [$ZnCl_2$] Odorless, white, crystalline granules. Incompatible with cyanides and sulfides. Decomposes to emit toxic chlorine and zinc oxide fumes when heated. Irritating and corrosive to the eyes, skin, and respiratory tract. Ingestion may cause vomiting and abdominal pain. *Not* listed as a RCRA Hazardous Waste.

Zinc Metal/Powder [Zn] A bluish-white lustrous metal. Moist zinc dust can ignite spontaneously in air. Forms flammable hydrogen gas in contact with alkali hydroxides, acids, or water. When heated to extreme temperatures, inhalation causes metal fume fever. *Not* listed as a RCRA Hazardous Waste.

Glossary of Terms and Abbreviations

Absolute. A chemical substance relatively free of impurities, e.g. absolute alcohol.

Absolute Pressure. The total pressure within a vessel, pipe, etc., not offset by external atmospheric pressure. See psia; psig.

Absorb. To soak up. The incorporation of a liquid into a solid substance, as by capillary, osmotic, solvent, or chemical action. See Adsorb.

ACGIH. American Conference of Governmental Industrial Hygienists. An organization of professionals in governmental agencies or educational institutions engaged in occupational safety and health programs. ACGIH develops and publishes recommended occupational exposure limits for chemical substances and physical agents. See TLV; BEI. (1330 Kemper Meadow Drive, Cincinnati, OH 45240; 513-742-2020)

Acid. An inorganic or organic compound that: 1) is usually corrosive to human tissue and must be handled with care; 2) has a pH of less than 7.0; 3) neutralizes bases (alkalis) to form salts; 4) dissociates in water yielding hydrogen or hydronium ions; 5) may react with metals to yield hydrogen; and 6) turns litmus paper red.

Acidosis. A condition of decreased alkalinity of the blood and tissues. Symptoms may include sickly sweet breath, headache, nausea, vomiting, visual disturbances; usually the result of excessive acid production. Tissues and central nervous system functions are disturbed.

Acrid. Irritating and bitter (usually referring to smell).

ACS, American Chemical Society. Professional society that establishes standards of purity for a number of reagents, e.g. the ACS Reagent Grade. They publish *Chemical Abstracts* and a host of professional journals and magazines dealing with various areas of chemistry, chemical engineering, and allied sciences. (1155 Sixteenth St., N.W., Washington, DC 20036; [202] 872-4567.)

Action Level. The exposure level (concentration in air) at which OSHA regulations to protect employees take effect (29 CFR 1910.1001-1047); e.g. workplace air analysis, employee training, medical monitoring, and recordkeeping. Exposure at or above action level is termed occupational exposure. Exposure below this level can also be harmful. This level is generally half the PEL.

Active Ingredient. The ingredient of a product that actually does what the product is designed to do.

Acute Exposure. Exposure of short duration, usually to relatively high concentrations or amounts of material.

Acute Health Effect. An adverse effect on a human or animal body, with symptoms developing rapidly. See Chronic Health Effect.

Acute Lethality. The death of animals immediately or within 14 days after a single dose of or exposure to a toxic substance.

Acute Toxicity. Adverse health effects resulting from brief exposure to a chemical (e.g. seconds, minutes, hours).

Administrative Controls. A number of measures used to reduce worker exposure, including work practices, labeling and warning devices, training, environmental monitoring, assignment scheduling, housekeeping, maintenance, and management.

Adsorb. To attract and retain gas or liquid molecules on the surface of another material. See Absorb.

Aerosol. A fine suspension in air or other gas of liquid (mist, fog) or solid (dust, fume, smoke) particles small enough to stay suspended. See Smoke; Fog; Mist.

Agent. Any substance, force, radiation, organism, or influence affecting the body. The effects may be beneficial or injurious.

AICS. Australian Inventory of Chemical Substances. This list contains chemical substances which can be used commercially in Australia. It is similar to TSCA Chemical Substances Inventory in the U.S.

ALARA. Acronym for "as low as reasonably achievable".

Alkali. An inorganic or organic chemical that: 1) is usually corrosive to human tissue and must be handled with care; 2) has a pH of more than 7.0; 3) neutralizes acids to form salts; 4) dissociates in water yielding hydroxide ions; 5) turns litmus paper blue; and 6) may also be called a base or caustic. Examples are oxides and hydroxides of certain metals belonging to group IA of the periodic table (Li, Na, K, Rb, Cs, Fr). Ammonia and amines may also be alkaline. Common commercial alkalis are sodium carbonate (soda ash), caustic soda and caustic potash, lime, lye, waterglass, regular mortar, Portland cement, and bicarbonate of soda. See Acid; Base; pH.

Allergen. A substance that causes an allergic reaction.

Allergy. A condition in which an initial symptomless exposure to a specific allergen later gives rise to a sensitivity to further exposure. Symptoms may be exhibited in a variety of ways, usually by respiratory distress or skin eruptions.

Alopecia. Loss of hair.

Ambient. Usual or surrounding conditions of temperature, humidity, etc.

Analgesia. Reduced sensitivity to pain.

Anesthesia. Loss of sensation, including loss of touch, pain, vibration sense, and/or temperature sense.

Anhydride. A compound derived from another compound (e.g. an acid) by removing the elements that compose water, i.e. hydrogen and oxygen.

Anhydrous. Without water. Describes a substance in which no water molecules are present in the form of a hydrate or as water of crystallization.

Anorexia. Loss of appetite.

Anosmia. Loss of the sense of smell.

Anoxia. A lack of oxygen in blood or tissues (literally, "without oxygen"). See Hypoxia.

ANSI. American National Standards Institute. A privately funded organization that identifies industrial/public national consensus standards and coordinates their development. Many ANSI standards relate to safe design/performance of equipment and safe practices or procedures. (1430 Broadway, New York, NY 10018; [212] 642-4900.)

Antidote. A remedy to counteract a poison's toxic effects; it may act to eliminate, absorb, or neutralize the poison.

Anuria. Absence or defective excretion of urine.

Apnea. Temporary stoppage of breathing.

Appearance. A material's physical state (solid, gas, or liquid), its color, and other visual attributes. If there is a difference between a material's appearance and that listed on the MSDS, contact your lab instructor.

AQTX, Aquatic Toxicity. The adverse effects on fresh or salt water life forms that result from exposure to a toxic substance. See TLm.

Aqueous, aq. Describes a water-based solution or suspension. Frequently describes a gaseous compound dissolved in water.

Argyria. Local or generalized gray-blue colored impregnation of body (skin) tissue with silver.

Article. A manufactured item that is specifically shaped or formed with its function dependent on its shape or design. Hazard laws exclude articles unless they give off harmful dust or fumes during their use.

Asbestosis. Chronic lung disease caused by inhaling airborne asbestos fibers.

Asphyxia. Lack of oxygen or inability of cells to use oxygen; simple asphyxia is suffocation caused by a lack of oxygen in the inhaled air (e.g. displacement by nitrogen); chemical asphyxia poisons the blood's ability to carry oxygen (carbon monoxide) or the cell's ability to use oxygen (cyanide).

Asphyxiant. Vapor or gas that can cause unconsciousness or death by suffocation (lack of oxygen). Most simple asphyxiants are harmful to the body only when they become so concentrated that they reduce (displace) available oxygen in the air (normally about 21%) to dangerous levels (18% or lower). Examples of simple asphyxiants are carbon dioxide, nitrogen, hydrogen, and helium. Chemical asphyxiants like carbon monoxide (CO) reduce the blood's ability to carry oxygen, or like cyanide, interfere with the body's utilization of oxygen.

Asphyxiation. A condition that causes asphyxia or suffocation. Asphyxiation is one of the principal potential hazards of working in confined spaces.

Aspiration Hazard. The danger of drawing material into the lungs, leading to an inflammatory response that can be fatal.

Asthma. A medical disorder which causes attacks of wheezing, chest tightness, shortness of breath, and/or coughing due to spasmodic contraction of the air passages.

ASTM. American Society for Testing and Materials. An organization that devises consensus standards for materials characterization and use. (100 Barr Harbor Dr., West Conshohocken, PA 19428; 610-832-9500)

Asymptomatic. Not exhibiting symptoms.

Ataxia. A loss of muscular coordination of gait or movement.

atm. Atmosphere. A unit of pressure equal to the average pressure that air exerts at sea level. 1 atm = 1.013×10^5 N/m^2, or 14.7 lb/in.^{2}, or 760 mm Hg or 10/kPa. Generally used in connection with high pressures.

Atrophy. Reduction in size or function of tissue, organs, or the entire body caused by lack of use.

Autoignition Temperature. The minimum temperature at which a substance ignites without application of a flame or spark. Do not heat materials to greater than 80% of this temperature.

BAL. British Anti-Lewisite. A name for the drug dimercaprol, a treatment for inhalation or ingestion of specific toxic metal compounds.

Base. An alkali. See Alkali.

Baumé, Bé. A scale of specific gravities devised by the French chemist Antoine Baumé (c. 1800; pronounced bo-may) that indicates concentration of materials in a solution. Baumé degree increases as specific gravity decreases.

BEI, Biological Exposure Indexes. Numerical values based on procedures to determine the amount of a material the human body absorbs by measuring the material or its metabolic products in tissue, fluid, or exhaled air. See the ACGIH publication *Documentation of the Threshold Limit Values and Biological Exposure Indices.*

Bioconcentration. The process by which a chemical is passed through the food chain from soil to plants and animals where it accumulates and is ultimately passed to humans.

Biodegradable. An organic material's capacity for decomposition as a result of attack by microorganisms. Sewage-treatment routines are based on this property. Biodegradable materials do not persist in nature.

Biological Monitoring. Analysis of body substances, such as blood or urine, to determine the extent of hazardous material absorption or accumulation.

BLEVE, Boiling Liquid Expanding Vapor Explosion. Used when describing fires involving compressed gases in cylinders that rupture due to extreme pressures and proceed to burn rapidly.

BOD, Biochemical Oxygen Demand. Amount of oxygen needed by bacteria to stabilize organic matter under aerobic conditions. Used to estimate degree of contamination in water supplies.

Body Burden. Total toxic material a person has ingested or inhaled from all sources over time and retained in the body. For example, lead can be ingested from drinking water channeled through lead-soldered pipes, lead glazes on dishes, or flakes from painted surfaces, or from many industrial operations.

Boiling Point, BP. The temperature at which a liquid's vapor pressure equals the surrounding atmospheric pressure so that the liquid rapidly vaporizes. Flammable materials with low BP's generally present special fire hazards [e.g. butane, BP = -0.5 °C (31 °F); gasoline, BP = 38 °C (100 °F)]. For mixtures, a range of temperature is given.

Bonding. A safety practice where two objects (tanks, cylinders, etc.) are interconnected with clamps and wire. This equalizes the electrical potential between the objects and helps prevent static sparks that can ignite flammable materials transferred between tanks. See Grounding.

BP. See Boiling Point.

Bradycardia. Slowed heartbeat (less than 60 beats per minute).

British Anti-Lewisite. See BAL.

Bronchitis. An inflammatory condition of the airways (bronchial tubes) resulting in coughing up of sputum.

Btu. British Thermal Unit. The quantity of heat required to raise the temperature of 1 lb of water from 17 °C (63 °F) to 18 °C (64 °F). Compare to Calorie.

Buffer. A substance that reduces the change in hydrogen ion concentration (pH) otherwise produced by adding acids or bases to a solution. A pH stabilizer.

Bulk Density. The mass (weight) per unit volume of a solid particulate material as it is normally packed, with voids between particulates containing air. Usually expressed as lb/ft^3 or g/cm^3.

Burning Rate. The time it takes a specified sized sample of solid material (e.g. 1" x 1") to burn a designated distance. The rate is given in units of distance/time.

c, ca. Circa, about, approximately.

C. Indicates continuous exposure when used with toxicological data; e.g. "LC_{50} > 5 mg/m^3, 24 h-C" means continuous exposure for 24 hours. OSHA also uses C to designate ceiling exposure limit. See Ceiling Limit; TLV.

°C. Degrees Celsius (centigrade). Metric temperature scale; 0 = water's freezing point, 100 = its boiling point. °F = (°C x 9/5) + 32. °C = (°F - 32) x 5/9. See °F.

CAA. *Clean Air Act.* Public Law PL 91-604, 40 CFR 50-80. EPA has jurisdiction. Effective Dec. 31, 1970, and significantly amended several times, most recently in 1990. The regulatory vehicle that sets limitations and monitors airborne pollution hazardous to public health or natural resources. The EPA sets national ambient air-quality standards. Enforcement and issuance of discharge permits are carried out by the states and are called state implementation plans. The CAA is directed toward by-products discharged into the air from stationary sources (i.e. factories) and mobile sources (i.e. automobiles) rather than use and assessment of specific chemicals.

Calorie. Unit of heat. The amount of heat required to raise 1 g of water 1 °C. Compare to Btu.

Cancer. An abnormal multiplication of cells that tends to infiltrate other tissues and metastasize (spread). Each cancer is believed to originate from a single "transformed" cell that grows (splits) at a fast, abnormally regulated pace, no matter where it occurs in the body.

Carcinogen. Material that either causes cancer in humans, or, because it causes cancer in animals, is considered capable of causing cancer in humans. A material is considered a carcinogen if 1) the International Agency for Research on Cancer (IARC) has evaluated and found it a carcinogen or potential carcinogen; 2) the National Toxicology Program's (NTP) *Annual Report on Carcinogens* lists it as a carcinogen or potential carcinogen; or 3) OSHA regulates it as a carcinogen.

Cardiovascular. System of the human body involving the heart and blood vessels.

CAS Number (CAS Registration Number). An assigned number used to identify a chemical. CAS stands for Chemical Abstracts Service, an organization that indexes information published in *Chemical Abstracts* by the American Chemical Society and that provides index guides by which information about particular substances may be located in the abstracts. Sequentially assigned CAS numbers identify specific chemicals, except when followed by an asterisk (*) that signifies a compound (often naturally occurring) of variable composition. The numbers have no chemical significance. The CAS number is a concise, unique means of material identification. (Chemical Abstracts Service, Division of American Chemical Society, Box 3012, Columbus, OH 43210; [614] 447-3600.)

Catalyst. A substance that modifies (slows, or more often quickens) a chemical reaction without being consumed in the reaction.

Cataract. A loss of transparency in the eye's crystalline lens or its capsule.

Caustic. See Alkali.

CC. Closed cup. Identifies one of the methods used to measure flash points of flammable liquids.

cc, cm^3. Cubic centimeter.

Ceiling Limit, C. The concentration not to exceed at any time. "An employee's exposure [to a hazardous material] shall at no time exceed the ceiling value" (OSHA).

Celsius. See °C.

Centigrade. See °C. Celsius is now this temperature scale's preferred name.

Centimeter, cm. 1/100 meter. A cm = approximately 0.4 in.

Centipoise, cP. A metric (cgs) unit of viscosity equal to 1/100 poise. The viscosity of water at 20 °C (68 °F) is almost 1 centipoise.

Central Nervous System (CNS). The brain and spinal cord.

Central Nervous System (CNS) Depression. Drowsiness, dizziness, and headache caused by a chemical acting on the brain; higher doses can cause unconsciousness, coma, or death.

CEPA, (Canada) Environmental Protection Act. Federal legislation, administered by Environment Canada, designed to protect the environment.

CERCLA. The *Comprehensive Environmental Response, Compensation, and Liability Act*. The Superfund Law, Public Law PL 96-510, found at 40 CFR 300. The EPA has jurisdiction. Enacted Dec. 11, 1980, and amended thereafter, CERCLA provides for identification and cleanup of hazardous materials released on the land and into the air, waterways, and groundwater. It covers areas affected by newly released materials and older leaking or abandoned dump sites. Report releases of hazardous materials to the National Response Center, (800) 424-8802. CERCLA established the superfund, a trust fund to help pay for cleanup of hazardous materials sites. The EPA has authority to collect cleanup costs from those who release the waste material. Cleanup funds come from fines and penalties, from taxes on chemical/petrochemical feed stocks, and the U.S. Treasury Department. A separate fund collects taxes on active disposal sites to finance monitoring after they close. CERCLA is a result of the serious problems that arose from the release of hazardous materials in the Love Canal area near Niagara Falls, NY, in August 1978.

CFC. Chlorofluorocarbon. Associated with damage to the Earth's ozone layer.

CFR. *Code of Federal Regulations.* A collection of the regulations established by law. Contact the agency that issued the regulation for details, interpretations, etc. Copies are sold by the Superintendent of Documents, Government Printing Office, Washington, DC 20402; (202) 512-1800.

cgs. Metric units of measure based upon centimeter, gram, and second.

Chelating Agent. A substance (e.g. EDTA) which can remove heavy metal toxins (such as lead, mercury, or arsenic) from the blood by complexing them and allowing their excretion in urine.

Chemical Cartridge Respirator. A respirator using various chemical substances to purify inhaled air of certain contaminative gases and vapors. Approved for concentrations no more than 10 times the TLV for a half facepiece and 100 times the TLV for a full facepiece, provided the contaminant has warning properties (odor or irritation) near the TLV.

Chemical Family. A group of single elements or compounds of a common general type. For example, acetone, methyl ethyl ketone (MEK), and methyl isobutyl ketone (MIBK) are of the ketone family; acrolein, furfural, and acetaldehyde are of the aldehyde family.

Chemical Formula. The number and kind of atoms comprising a molecule of a material. Water's chemical formula is H_2O. Each water molecule consists of 2 atoms of hydrogen and 1 atom of oxygen.

Chemical Hygiene Officer. Per 29 CFR 1910.1450; OSHA's *Occupational Exposures to Hazardous Chemicals in Laboratories* standard. The designated, qualified employee who assists in the development and implementation of the CHP. See CHP.

Chemical Name. A chemical's scientific name. Complex chemicals may have more than one name, corresponding to different naming systems.

Chemical Pneumonitis. Inflammation of the lungs caused by inhaling a chemical that is irritating or otherwise toxic to the lungs.

Chemical Reactivity. A chemical's tendency to react with other materials. Undesirable and dangerous effects such as heat, explosions, or production of noxious substances can result.

Chemiluminescence. Emission of light during a chemical reaction other than burning.

CHEMTREC. Chemical Transportation Emergency Center. Established in Washington, DC, by the Chemical Manufacturers Association (CMA) to provide emergency information on materials involved in transportation accidents. 24-hour number: (800) 424-9300.

Chloracne. A severe form of skin acne caused by exposure to certain chlorinated chemical compounds.

CHP, Chemical Hygiene Plan. Per 29 CFR 1910.1450, OSHA's *Occupational Exposures to Hazardous Chemicals in Laboratories* standard. Effective May 1, 1990. A written plan that includes specific work practices, standard operating procedures, equipment, engineering controls, and policies to ensure that employees are protected from hazardous exposure levels to all potentially hazardous chemicals in use in their work area. This OSHA standard provides for training, employee access to information, medical consultations, examinations, hazard identification procedures, respirator use, and recordkeeping practices. See paragraph E of the standard.

Chronic Exposure. Continuous or intermittent exposure extending over a long time period, usually applies to relatively low material amounts or concentrations.

Chronic Health Effect. An adverse effect on a human or animal body with symptoms that develop slowly over a long time period and persist or that recur frequently. See Acute Health Effect.

Chronic Toxicity. Adverse health effects resulting from long-term exposure to a chemical (e.g. months, years, decades).

Clastogenic. An agent that causes damage to genetic material (i.e. breakage or disruption of chromosomes).

Closed Cup. See CC.

Closed System. Equipment designed and used so that there is no release of the chemical into the surrounding environment.

CNS. See Central Nervous System.

CNS Depression. See Central Nervous System Depression.

CO, Carbon Monoxide. A colorless, odorless, flammable, and very toxic gas produced by incomplete combustion of carbon compounds and as a by-product of many chemical processes. A chemical asphyxiant, it reduces the blood's ability to carry oxygen. Hemoglobin absorbs CO 200 times more readily than it does oxygen.

CO_2, Carbon Dioxide. A dense, colorless gas produced by combustion and decomposition of organic substances and as a by-product of many chemical processes. CO_2 does not burn and is relatively nontoxic and unreactive. High concentrations, especially in confined places, can create hazardous oxygen-deficient environments that can cause asphyxiation. CO_2 is 1.5 times as dense as air, making it useful as a fire-extinguishing agent to block oxygen and smother a fire.

COD, Chemcial Oxygen Demand. The amount of oxygen required under designated test conditions to oxidate waterborne organic and inorganic material. Used in measuring the degree of pollution in domestic and industrial waters.

Code of Federal Regulations. See CFR.

Coefficient of Water/Oil Distribution. Also called the partition coefficient, it is the ratio of the solubility of a chemical in water to its solubility in oil. Used to indicate how easily human or other organisms can absorb or store a material. Sometimes abbreviated Ko/w; may also be expressed as its logarithm, log Ko/w.

Coma. Extended loss of consciousness due to an injury, illness, or poison.

Combustible. A material that will burn under most conditions and may ignite easily depending on its flash point. The DOT defines a combustible liquid as a liquid with a flash above 141 °F (60.5 °C) and below 200 °F (93 °C). Both NFPA and OSHA generally define a combustible liquid as a liquid with a flash point at or above 100 °F (38 °C). See Flammable; Flammable Liquid.

Common Name. A designation for a material other than its chemical name, such as code name or code number or trade, brand, or generic name. May be used as the "product identifier" in Canadian law [*Workplace Hazardous Materials Information System* (WHMIS) regulations].

Compressed Gas. Any material contained under pressure, i.e., dissolved gas or liquefied by compression or refrigeration.

conc. Concentration.

Conjunctivitis. Irritation and inflammation of the lining of the eye and eyelids.

Consumer Products Safety Commission. See CPSC.

Convulsions. Violent body spasms; fits or seizures.

Cornea. Transparent structure of the eyeball's external layer.

Corrosion Rate. Expressed in inches or millimeters of steel (or other defined material) per year, at a stated temperature.

Corrosive. A liquid or solid that causes visible destruction of, or irreversible alterations in, living tissue by chemical action at the site of contact; or a liquid that causes a severe corrosion rate on steel or aluminum.

cP. See Centipoise.

CPSC. Consumer Products Safety Commission. A Federal agency responsible for regulating hazardous materials when they are used in consumer goods per the *Hazardous Substances Act and Poison Prevention Packaging Act* of 1970.

Critical Pressure/Critical Temperature. A temperature above which a gas cannot be liquefied by pressure. The critical pressure is that pressure required to liquefy a gas at its critical temperature.

Cryogenic. Relating to extremely low temperature. For example, refrigerated gases are cryogenic materials that can cause frostbite on contact.

cu ft, ft^3. Cubic foot. Cu ft is more usual.

cu m, m^3. Cubic meter. m^3 is preferred.

Cutaneous. Pertaining to the skin (dermal).

CVS. Cardiovascular system (heart and blood vessels).

CWA. *Clean Water Act.* Public Law PL 92-500. Found at 40 CFR 100-140 and 400-470. Effective November 18, 1972, and amended significantly since then. EPA and Army Corps of Engineers have jurisdiction. CWA regulates the discharge of nontoxic and toxic pollutants into surface waters. Its ultimate goal is to eliminate all discharges into surface waters. Its interim goal is to make surface waters usable for fishing, swimming, etc. EPA sets guidelines, and states issue permits (NPDES, Natural Pollutant Discharge Elimination System permit) specifying the types of control equipment and discharges for each facility.

Cyanosis. A dark blue to purplish coloration of the skin and the mucous membrane caused by lack of oxygen utilization by the body.

Dangerously Reactive Material. A material that can react by itself (e.g. polymerize) or with air or water to produce a hazardous condition. Preventive measures can be taken if you know what conditions may cause the dangerous reaction.

Dec, Decomp. Decompose, decomposition. Breakdown of a material (by heat, chemical reaction, electrolysis, decay, or other processes) into parts, elements, or simpler compounds.

Deliquescent. A term used to characterize water-soluble salts (usually powdered) that tend to absorb moisture from the air and to soften or dissolve as a result. See Hygroscopic; Hydrophilic.

Demulcent. A material capable of soothing or protecting inflamed, irritated mucous membranes.

Density. Ratio of weight (mass) to volume of a material, usually in grams per cubic centimeter or pounds per gallon. See Specific Gravity; Bulk Density.

Dermal. Pertaining to the skin (cutaneous).

Dermal Toxicity. Adverse effects resulting from a material's absorption through skin. Ordinarily used to denote effects on experimental animals.

Dermatitis. Skin rash; inflammation of the skin.

Designated Area. An area of (or device within) a lab to be used for work with select carcinogens, reproductive toxins, and other materials that have a high degree of acute toxicity. An administrative control intended to minimize the potential for employee exposure to hazardous chemicals.

Diaphoresis. Perspiration, especially profuse.

Dilution Ventilation. See General Ventilation.

DOT. U.S. Department of Transportation. Regulates transportation of materials to protect the public as well as fire, law, and other emergency-response personnel. DOT classifications specify the use of appropriate warnings, such as oxidizing agent or flammable liquid. (400 7th St., SW, Washington, DC 20590.)

DOT Identification Numbers. Four-digit numbers used to identify particular materials for regulation of their transportation. See DOT publications that describe the regulations (49 CFR 172.101). These numbers are called product identification numbers (PINs) under the Canadian *Transportation of Dangerous Goods* regulations. Those numbers used internationally may carry a UN prefix (e.g. UN 1170, ethyl alcohol), but those used only in North America have an NA prefix (e.g. NA 9163, zirconium sulfate).

Dust. Solid particles suspended in air, often produced by some mechanical process such as crushing, grinding, abrading, or blasting. Dusts may be inhalation, fire, or dust-explosion hazards.

Dysplasia. Abnormal growth or development of organs or cells.

Dyspnea. A sense of difficulty in breathing; shortness of breath.

Dysuria. Difficult or painful urination.

EC_{50}. (Median) effective concentration. The concentration of a material in water, a single dose of which is expected to cause a biological effect on 50% of a group of test animals.

Eczema. A skin rash characterized by redness, itching, sometimes blistering; may become scaly or crusty.

ED_{50}. (Median) effective dose, usually expressed in mg/kg, that produced a specified effect in 50% of the test population.

Edema. Swelling due to accumulation of fluid in tissues.

EEC. European Economic Community.

EINECS. The European Inventory of Existing Chemical Substances. A list of chemical substances identified by CAS and EINECS numbers that were marketed in the European Community between 1/1/71 and 9/18/81.

Electrolyte. A substance (as an acid, base, salt) that dissociates into ions when in aqueous solution and that provides ionic conductivity. Electrolytes are lost from the body through perspiration as salts, causing impairment of central nervous system functions if not adequately replaced.

ELINICS. A list of approximately 400 chemicals identified by EINECS numbers, established with the European Community from 9/18/81 to 6/30/90. The list was published on 5/29/91 and is a supplement to EINECS. Additional supplements will be added as necessary.

Embolism. Obstruction of a blood vessel by a transported clot, a mass of bacteria, etc.

Embryo. An organism in the early stages of development before birth. In humans, the developing child is considered an embryo from conception to the end of the second month of pregnancy.

Embryotoxin. A material harmful to a developing embryo at a concentration that has no adverse effect on the pregnant female.

Emetic. An agent, such as syrup of ipecac, which induces vomiting. *Never* use an emetic if victim is not alert or after ingestion of solvents; *always* seek medical advice before giving an emetic.

Emphysema. An irreversible lung condition in which the alveolar walls lose resiliency, resulting in excessively reduced lung capacity.

Endothermic. A chemical reaction that absorbs heat.

Engineering Controls. Engineering control systems reduce potential hazards by isolating the worker from the hazard or by removing the hazard from the work environment. Methods include substitution, ventilation, isolation, and enclosure.

This is preferred over administrative controls and personal protective equipment.

EP. Extreme pressure.

EPA, (U.S.) Environmental Protection Agency. A Federal agency with environmental protection regulatory and enforcement authority. Administers the CAA, CWA, RCRA, TSCA, and other Federal environmental laws. (400 M Street, Washington, DC 20460; [202] 382-2090)

Epidemiology. The study of the relationships between diseases and the various factors that could determine their frequency and distribution in populations.

Epiphora. Excessive flow of tears.

Epistaxis. Nosebleed.

Ergonomics. The study of human characteristics for appropriate design of living and work environments.

Erythema. Redness of the skin; usually due to a local increase in blood flow.

Etiology. All of the factors that contribute to the cause of a disease or an abnormal condition.

Evaporation Rate. The rate at which a material vaporizes (volatilizes, evaporates) from the liquid or solid state when compared to a known material's vaporization rate. Evaporation rate is useful in evaluating a material's health and fire hazards. The known reference material is usually normal butyl acetate (*N*-BuAc or *n*-BuAc), with a vaporization rate designated as 1.0. Vaporization rates of other solvents or materials are then classified as: 1) Fast evaporating if greater than 3.0, e.g. methyl ethyl ketone (MEK), 3.8; acetone, 5.6; hexane, 8.3; 2) Medium evaporating if 0.8 to 3.0, e.g. 190-proof (95%) ethyl alcohol, 1.4; VM&P naphtha, 1.4; MIBK, 1.6; 3) Slow evaporating if less than 0.8, e.g. xylene, 0.6; isobutyl alcohol, 0.6; normal butyl alcohol, 0.4; water, 0.3; mineral spirits, 0.1.

Explosive. A material that produces a sudden, almost instantaneous release of pressure, gas, and heat when subjected to abrupt shock, high temperature, or an ignition source.

Explosive Limits. See Flammable Limits.

Exposure Limits. The concentration in workplace air of a chemical deemed the maximum acceptable. This means that most workers can be exposed at given levels or lower without harmful effects. Exposure limits in common use are: 1) TLV-TWA (threshold limit value - time-weighted average); 2) STEL (short-term exposure limit); and 3) C (ceiling value).

Exothermic. A chemical reaction that gives off heat.

Extinguishing Media, Agents. Type of fire extinguisher or extinguishing method appropriate for a specific material. Some chemicals react violently in the presence of water, so other methods, such as foam or CO_2, should be followed.

°F or F. Degrees Fahrenheit. See °C.

f/cc. Fibers per cubic centimeter of air.

Fasciculation. Muscular twitching.

***Federal Register* (U.S.).** See FR.

Fiber. A basic form of matter, usually crystalline, with a high ratio of length to diameter. Examples: animal (wool); vegetable (cotton); mineral (asbestos, steel); and synthetic (rayon, carbon, high polymers).

Fibrosis. Scarring; scarring in the lungs may affect oxygenation of blood.

FIFRA. The Federal Insecticide, Fungicide, and Rodenticide Act. Enacted on 10/21/72, this act provides the regulatory authority for registration and use of pesticides and similar products intended to kill or control insects, rodents, and weeds.**Fines.** Finely crushed or powdered material or fibers; especially those smaller than the average in a mix of various sizes.

Fire Diamond (NFPA Hazard Rating). The National Fire Protection Agency (NFPA) visual rating system that addresses the health, flammability, reactivity, and related hazards of a material which may exist due to short-term, acute exposure caused by a fire, spill, or similar emergency. Per "NFPA 704" publication.
Position A - Health Hazard (*Blue*). Degree of hazard; level of short-term protection
0 = Ordinary Combustible Hazards in a Fire
1 = Slightly Hazardous
2 = Hazardous
3 = Extreme Danger
4 = Deadly

Position B - Flammability (*Red*). Susceptibility to burning
0 = Will Not Burn
1 = Will Ignite if Preheated
2 = Will Ignite if Moderately Heated
3 = Will Ignite at Most Ambient Conditions
4 = Burns Readily at Ambient Conditions
Position C - Reactivity, Instability (*Yellow*). Energy released if burned, decomposed, or mixed
0 = Stable and Not Reactive with Water
1 = Unstable if Heated
2 = Violent Chemical Change
3 = Shock and Heat May Detonate
4 = May Detonate
Position D - Special Hazard (*White*).
OX = Oxidizer
W = Use No Water, reacts!

Fire Point. The lowest temperature at which a liquid produces sufficient vapor to flash near its surface and continues to burn. Usually 10 to 30 °C higher than the flash point.

First Aid. Immediate measures that can be taken by the victim or others in order to reduce or eliminate the potential effects of a chemical exposure or other injury.

Flammable. Describes any solid, liquid, vapor, or gas that ignites easily and burns rapidly. See Combustible; Flammable Liquid; and Inflammabe.

Flammable Aerosol. A material is considered a flammable aerosol if it is packaged in an aerosol container and can release a flammable material.

Flammable Gas. A gas that at normal atmospheric pressure forms a flammable mixture with air at a concentration of 13% by volume or less; or over a concentration range greater than 12% by volume, regardless of lower limit.

Flammable Limits (Flammability Limits, Explosive Limits). Minimum and maximum concentrations of a flammable gas or vapor between which ignition can occur. Concentrations below the lower flammable limit (LFL) are too lean to burn, while concentrations above the upper flammable limit (UFL) are too rich. All concentrations between LFL and UFL are in the flammable range, and special precautions are needed to prevent ignition or explosion.

Flammable Liquid. A liquid that gives off vapors readily ignitable at room temperature. The DOT defines a flammable liquid as a liquid with a flash point of not more than 141 °F (60.5 °C). The NFPA and OSHA generally define a flammable liquid as a liquid with a flash point below 100 °F (37.8 °C).

Flammable Solid. A solid, other than an explosive or blasting agent, that ignites readily and continues to burn so vigorously and persistently that it creates a serious hazard. Flammable solids are liable to cause fires under ordinary conditions or during transportation, through friction, as a result of spontaneous chemical change, or from retained heat from manufacturing or processing, or moisture absorption.

Flash Back. Occurs when a distant spark or ignition source ignites a trail of flammable material (e.g. gasoline vapor). The flame then travels along the trail of the material back to its source.

Flash Point, FP. Lowest temperature at which a flammable liquid gives off sufficient vapor to form an ignitable mixture with air near its surface or within a vessel. Combustion does not continue. FP is determined by laboratory tests in cups. See Fire Point.

Foam. Fire-fighting material consisting of water and foaming agents into which air is blown, producing a voluminous, stable blanket of bubbles. The foam clings to vertical and horizontal surfaces and flows freely over burning materials. Foam puts out a fire by blanketing it, excluding air, and blocking escape of volatile vapor. Its flowing properties resist mechanical interruption and reseal the burning material.

Fog. A visible suspension of fine droplets of liquid in a gas; e.g. water in air.

Formula Mass. The sum of atomic weights of the atoms in a molecule. For example, water (H_2O) has a formula mass of 18.0, the atomic weights being [hydrogen: 2(1.0) + oxygen: 16] = 18.

FP. See Flash Point.

FR. *Federal Register.* A daily publication that lists and discusses Federal regulations. Available from the Government Printing Office.

Freezing Point. The temperature at which a material changes from a liquid to a solid state upon cooling. This information is important because a frozen material may burst its container or the hazards could change.

Fugitive Emission. Gas, liquid, solid, vapor, fume, mist, fog, or dust that escapes from process equipment or a product.

Full Protective Clothing. Fully protective gear that prevents skin contact with, inhalation of, or ingestion of gases, vapor, liquids, and solids (dusts, etc.). Includes SCBA (self-contained breathing apparatus).

Fumes. Tiny solid particles formed by the vaporization of a solid which then condenses in air; particles are usually of a size which readily reach the air sacs (alveoli) of the lungs.

g. Gram. Metric unit of weight. See kg.

Gangrene. Death of tissue leading to its rotting.

Gas. A formless fluid which disperses in air; often found in tanks or cylinders and may be created by a chemical reaction. It can be changed to its liquid or solid state only by increased pressure and/or decreased temperature.

Gastric Lavage. Washing out of the stomach using a tube and fluids. Pumping the stomach.

Gastroenteritis. Stomach and intestine inflammation.

Gastrointestinal Tract. GI tract. The stomach and intestine as a functional unit.

Gavage. Feeding by means of a stomach tube.

General Ventilation. Also known as dilution ventilation. The removal of contaminated air and its replacement with clean air from the general workplace area as opposed to local ventilation, which is specific air changing in the immediate area of a contamination source. An example of local ventilation is a laboratory fume hood.

Generic Name. A common, possibly chemical, name applied generally to a substance. For example, bleach is the generic name for the chemical sodium hypochlorite. Chlorox™ is a tradename for bleach. A chemical name may be used as a generic name, but tradenames are not generic names.

Gestation. The development of the fetus in the womb from conception to birth (i.e. pregnancy).

GI, GIT. See Gastrointestinal Tract.

Gingivitis. Inflammation of the gums.

GRAS. Generally recognized as safe. A phrase applied to food additives approved by the Food and Drug Administration (FDA).

Grounding. A safety practice to conduct any electrical charge to the ground, preventing sparks that could ignite a flammable material. See Bonding.

h, hr(s). Hour(s).

Hazard Communication Rule. Requires chemical manufacturers and importers to assess the hazards associated with the materials in their workplace (29 CFR 1910.1200). Material safety data sheets, labeling, and training are all results of this law. See *OSH Act.*

Hazardous Chemical, Material. In a broad sense, any substance or mixture of substances having properties capable of producing adverse effects on the health or safety of a human. In 1971, OSHA adopted the following definition in regulations affecting employers in operations subject to the *Federal Longshoremen's and Harbor Worker's Compensation Act.* "The term hazardous material means a material which has one or more of these characteristics: 1) Has a flash point below 60 °C (140 °F), closed cup, or is subject to spontaneous heating; 2) Has a threshold limit value below 400 ppm for gases and vapors, below 15 mg/m^3 for fumes, and below 25 mppcf (million particles per cubic foot) for dusts; 3) Has a single dose oral LD_{50} below 500 mg/kg; 4) Is subject to polymerization with the release of large amounts of energy; 5) Is a strong oxidizing or reducing agent; 6) Causes first-degree burns to skin [from a] short time exposure, or is systemically toxic by skin contact; or 7) In the course of normal operations, may produce dusts, gases, fumes, vapors, mists, or smokes that have one or more of the above characteristics." Included are substances that are carcinogens, toxic, irritants, corrosives, sensitizers, and agents that damage the lungs, skin, eyes, mucous membranes, etc.

Hazardous Decomposition. A breaking down or separation of a substance into its constituent parts, elements, or into simpler compounds accompanied by the release of heat, gas, or hazardous materials.

Hazardous Decomposition Products. Hazardous products resulting from decomposition of a material. For example, vinyl chloride, a compound widely used to make plastics, releases poisonous hydrogen chloride, carbon monoxide, and phosgene gases when burned.

Hazard Warning. Defined by OSHA as "any words, pictures, symbols, or combination thereof appearing on a label or other appropriate form of warning which convey the hazard(s) of the chemical(s) in the container(s)."

Hazardous Waste Number. An identification number assigned by the EPA, per the RCRA law (40 CFR 261.33, 40 CFR 302.4), to identify and track wastes.

Health Surveillance. The continuing scrutiny of specific individuals for the purpose of identifying disorders or health states, especially those that may relate to exposure to hazardous materials.

Hematuria. Blood in the urine.

Hemolysis. Destruction of red blood cells leading to release of hemoglobin.

HEPA. High-efficiency particulate air filter. Also called absolute. Has a 99.97% removal efficiency for 0.3-micron particles.

Hepatic. Pertaining to the liver.

HMIS. The hazardous materials identification system developed by the National Paint and Coatings Association (NPCA) to provide information on the acute health, reactivity, and flammability hazards encountered in the workplace. This system also includes temperatures under fire conditions (especially for flammability and reactivity). A number is assigned to a material indicating degree of hazard, from 0 for the least up to 4 for the most severe. Letters designate personal protective equipment. (Details available from Labelmaster, 5724 N Pulaski Rd, Chicago, IL 60646; [312] 478-0900.) See NPCA.

Hydrolysis. The process by which a chemical compound is decomposed by reaction with water.

Hydrophilic. Describing materials having large molecules that tend to absorb and retain water, causing them to swell and frequently to gel. See Deliquescent.

Hygroscopic. Readily adsorbing available moisture in any form. See Deliquescent.

Hyperemia. Congestion of blood in a body part.

Hypergolic. Self-igniting upon contact of its components without a spark or external aid; especially rocket fuel or a propellant that consists of combinations of fuels and oxidizers.

Hypocalcemia. Calcium deficiency of the blood.

Hypoxia. Insufficient oxygen reaching the tissues of the body. See Anoxia.

I. Intermittent.

IARC. International Agency for Research on Cancer. One of the three sources that OSHA refers to for data on a material's carcinogenicity. (World Health Organization, Geneva, Switzerland; distributed in the USA from 49 Sheridan Avenue, Albany, NY 12210 [518] 436-9686.)

IDLH. Immediately dangerous to life and health. The maximum concentration from which one could escape within 30 minutes without any escape-impairing symptoms or irreversible health effects. Used to determine respirator selection. (Note: Carcinogenic effects were not considered in setting these values.)

Ignition Temperature. The lowest temperature at which a combustible material ignites in air and continues to burn independently of the heat source.

Impervious. Describes a material that does not allow another substance to penetrate or pass through it.

Incompatible. Describes materials that could cause dangerous reactions and the release of energy from direct contact with one another.

Inert Ingredients. Anything other than the active ingredient in a product; not having active properties. Inert ingredients may be hazardous. For example, the propellant gas in aerosol spray, such as hair spray, may be flammable.

Inflammable. Capable of being easily set on fire and continue burning, especially violently. *Do not confuse with nonflammable.* See Combustible; Flammable.

Inflammation. A local response to cellular injury due to trauma, infection, or chemical irritation; symptoms include swelling, redness, pain, tenderness, and loss of function.

Ingestion. Swallowing a chemical substance; may inadvertently result from eating, drinking, or smoking in the workplace or with contaminated hands.

Inhalation. Entry of a chemical substance to the lungs by breathing.

Inhibitor. A material added to another to prevent an unwanted reaction; e.g. polymerization.

Inorganic Materials. Compounds derived from other than vegetable or animal sources that do not generally contain carbon atoms. Some simple carbon compounds are considered inorganic (e.g., CO_2, carbonates, cyanides).

Insol. Insoluble.

Interstitial Fibrosis. Scarring of the lungs.

Intraperitoneal. A route of administration for toxicological studies. A material is injected into the peritoneal (abdominal/pelvic) cavity.

Iodism. An abnormal condition resulting from prolonged (chronic) exposure to iodine or its compounds. Characterized by emaciation, skin eruptions, headache, excess salivation, runny nose, and sneezing.

Iridocyclitis. Inflammation of both the eye's iris and its ciliary body.

Irritant. A substance capable of causing a reversible or irreversible inflammatory effect on living tissue by chemical action at the site of contact as a function of concentration or duration of exposure.

Isomers. Chemical compounds with the same molecular weight and atomic composition but differing molecular structure; e.g. *n*-pentane and 2-methylbutane.

I.V. Intravenous. Injection of a substance into a vein.

Jaundice. Yellowish discoloration of tissue (skin), whites of eyes (sclera), and bodily fluids with bile pigment (bilirubin) caused by liver damage, gall bladder disease, or hemolysis.

Ketosis. The condition marked by excessive production or accumulation of ketone bodies in the body caused by disturbed carbohydrate metabolism.

kg, kilogram. 1000 gram.

L, l. Liter. Basic metric unit of volume. One liter of water weighs 1 kg and is equal to 1.057 quarts.

Label. Any written, printed, or graphic sign or symbol displayed on or affixed to containers of hazardous chemicals. A label should identify the hazardous material, appropriate hazard warnings, and name and address of the chemical manufacturer, importer, or other responsible party.

Laboratory. Per 29 CFR 1910.1450, a facility where "laboratory use of hazardous chemicals" occurs; where relatively small quantities of hazardous chemicals are used on a non-production basis.

Laboratory Scale (Activity). The work involves containers of substances used for reactions and transfers that are designed for easy and safe handling by one person. Workplaces that produce commercial quantities of materials are excluded from the definition of "Laboratory".

Laboratory-type Hood. An enclosed lab cabinet with a moveable sash or fixed access port on the front, connected to a ventilating system that may incorporate air scrubbing or filtering facilities. In operation it draws in and then exhausts air from the lab to prevent or minimize the escape of air contaminants. It enables employees to manipulate materials in the hood using only their hands and arms. Walk-in hoods are permitted if airflow and exhaust remove contaminants and the employee is not within the enclosure when contaminants are released.

Laboratory Use. (Of hazardous chemicals) is when all of these conditions are met: a) chemical manipulations are carried out on a "laboratory scale"; b) multiple chemical procedures or chemicals are used; c) the procedures are neither part of nor simulate a production process; and d) protective lab practices and equipment are available and in common use to minimize the potential for employee exposure to hazardous chemicals.

Lacrimation. Secretion and discharge of tears.

Lacrimator. A material that, upon exposure to it, causes tears.

Landfill. Disposal of trash and waste products at a controlled location that is then sealed and buried under earth. Increasingly seen as a less than satisfactory disposal method because of the long-term environmental impact of waste materials in the ground.

Latency Period. Time that elapses between exposure and first manifestations of disease or illness. Latency periods can range from minutes to decades, depending on the hazardous material and disease produced.

Lavage. Rinse with water.

Lay Language. Language that is easily understood by the general public without specialized training.

LC_{50}. Lethal concentration 50, median lethal concentration. The concentration of a material in air that on the basis of laboratory tests (respiratory route) is expected to kill 50% of a group of test animals when administered as a single exposure in a specific time period, usually 1 hour. LC_{50} is expressed as parts of material per million parts of air; by volume (ppm) for gases and vapors; as micrograms of material per liter of air (μg/l); or milligrams of material per cubic meter of air (mg/m^3) for dusts and mists, as well as for gases and vapors.

LC_{Lo}. Lethal concentration low. The lowest concentration of a substance in air reported to have caused death in humans or animals. The reported concentrations may be entered for periods of exposure that are less than 24 hours (acute) or greater than 24 hours (subacute and chronic).

LD_{50}. Lethal dose 50. The single dose of a substance that causes the death of 50% of an animal population from exposure to the substance by any route other than inhalation. LD_{50} is usually expressed as milligrams or grams of material per kilogram of animal weight (mg/kg or g/kg). The animal species and means of administering the dose (oral, intravenous, etc.) should also be stated.

LD_{Lo}. Lethal dose low. The lowest dose of a substance introduced by any route, other than inhalation, reported to have caused death in humans or animals.

Leaching. The movement of a substance down through or out of soil as a result of its mixing and moving with water. Important when assessing a material's ability to contaminate groundwater.

LEL. See Lower Explosive Limit; Lower Flammable Limit.

Lesion. An abnormal change, injury, or damage to tissue or to an organ.

Lethargy. A sense of fatigue, drowsiness, and laziness.

Leukemia. A progressive, malignant disease of the blood-forming organs.

LFL. See Lower Flammable Limit; Lower Explosive Limit.

LFM or lfm. Linear feet per minute.

Limits of Flammability. See Flammable Limits.

Lipid Granuloma. A mass of chronically inflamed tissue, usually infective.

Lipid Pneumonia. A chronic condition caused by aspiration of oily substances into the lungs.

Local Ventilation. The drawing off of contaminated air directly from its source. This type of ventilation is recommended for hazardous airborne materials. Treatment of exhausted air to remove contaminants may be required.

Lower Explosive Limit, Lower Flammable Limit. Refers to the lowest concentration of gas or vapor (% by volume in air) that burns or explodes if an ignition source is present at ambient temperatures. See Flammable Limits.

m. Meter. The basic metric measure of length; equivalent to 39.371 in.

m^3 or cu m. Cubic meter; m^3 is preferred.

Malaise. A vague, generalized, ill feeling.

Material Safety Data Sheet. See MSDS.

Maximum Safe Storage Temperature (MSST). See SADT (Self-Accelerating Decomposition Temperature).

Melting Point. The temperature above which a solid changes to a liquid upon heating.

Mercaptans. A group of organic compounds resembling alcohols, but with sulfur replacing the oxygen of the hydroxyl group. For example, ethanethiol [C_2H_5SH].

Metabolism. The process of change some chemicals go through after absorption by the body.

Metastasis. The transmission of a disease from one part of the body to another.

Meter. The basic measure of length; equivalent to 39.371 in.

Methemoglobinemia. The presence of methemoglobin in the bloodstream caused by the reaction of materials with the hemoglobin in red blood cells that reduces their oxygen-carrying capacity. Methemoglobin is a soluble, brown, crystalline blood pigment that differs from hemoglobin in that it contains the iron (III) ion instead of iron (II) and is unable to combine reversibly with molecular oxygen.

mg. Milligram (1/1000, 10^{-3}, of a gram).

mg/kg. Milligram per kilogram. Dosage used in toxicology testing to indicate a dose administered per kg of body weight.

mg/m^3. Milligram per cubic meter of air. $mg/m^3 = ppm \times MW/24.45$ at 25 °C.

Microgram (µg). One-millionth (10^{-6}) of a gram.

Micrometer (µm). One-millionth (10^{-6}) of a meter; often referred to as a micron.

micron, µ. See Micrometer.

Millimeter (mm). 1/1000 (10^{-3}) of a meter.

min. Minute.

Mine Safety and Health Administration. See MSHA.

Miscible. When two liquids or two gases are completely soluble in each other in all proportions. While gases mix with one another in all proportions, the miscibility of liquids depends on their chemical natures.

Mist. Suspended liquid droplets in air generated by condensation from a gaseous to liquid state or by mechanically breaking up a liquid by splashing or atomizing.

Mixture. A heterogeneous association of materials that cannot be represented by a chemical formula and that does not undergo chemical change due to interaction among the mixed materials. The constituent materials may or may not be uniformly dispersed and can usually be separated by mechanical means (as opposed to a chemical reaction). Uniform liquid mixtures are called solutions. "If a hazardous chemical is present in the mixture in reportable quantities (i.e. 0.1% for carcinogens and 1.0% for other health hazards), it must be reported unless the mixture has been tested as a whole" (OSHA CPL 23-02.38A).

ml. Milliliter. One thousandth of a liter. A metric unit of capacity, for all practical purposes equal to 1 cubic centimeter. One cubic inch is about 16 ml.

MLD. Mild irritation effects.

mm Hg. A measure of pressure in millimeters of a mercury column above a reservoir, or difference of level in a U-tube. See atm.

MOD. Moderate irritation effects.

Mole or mol. The quantity of a chemical substance that has a mass in grams numerically equal to the formula mass. For example, table salt (NaCl) has a formula mass of 58.5 (Na, 23, and Cl, 35.5). Thus, one mole of NaCl is 58.5 g.

Molecular Weight. See Formula Mass.

Molecule. The smallest representative particle of a covalently bonded chemical compound.

mppcf. Millions of particles per cubic foot of air, based on impinger samples counted by light-field techniques (OSHA).

MSDS. Material safety data sheet. A fact sheet summarizing information about material identification; hazardous ingredients; health, physical, and fire hazards; first aid; chemical reactivities and incompatibilities; spill leak, and disposal procedures; and protective measures required for safe handling and storage. OSHA has established guidelines for descriptive data that should be concisely provided on a data sheet to serve as the basis for written hazard communication programs. The thrust of the law is to have those who make, distribute, and use hazardous materials responsible for effective communication. See *Hazard Communication Rule*, 29 CFR, Part 1910.1200, as amended, Sec. g. See also Schedule I, Sec. 12, of the *Canadian Hazardous Products Act*. The CMA has recently drawn up a set of guidelines for developing a consistent MSDS format. This standard format has been accepted by ANSI.

MSHA. Mine Safety and Health Administration. A Federal agency within the U.S. Department of Labor that devises and promulgates mandatory safety and health rules for mines.

MSST, Maximum Safe Storage Temperature. See SADT (Self-Accelerating Decomposition Temperature).

Mucous Membrane. The mucous-secreting membrane lining the hollow organs of the body, i.e. nose, mouth, stomach, intestine, bronchial tubes, urinary tract.

Mutagen. A material that induces genetic changes (mutations) in the DNA of chromosomes. Chromosomes are the "blueprints" of life within individual cells. Mutagens may affect future generations if sperm or egg cells are affected.

MW. See Molecular Weight.

N (Newton). The metric unit of force, approximately equal to the weight of a 102.5 g mass.

***n*-.** Normal. A chemical name prefix signifying a straight-chain structure; i.e. no branches.

NA, ND. Not applicable, not available; not determined.

NA Number. See DOT Identification Numbers.

Narcosis. Sleepiness or a state of unconsciousness caused by a chemical.

National Fire Protection Association. See NFPA.

National Toxicology Program. See NTP.

Nausea. A tendency to vomit; a feeling of sickness in the stomach.

NCI. National Cancer Institute. A part of the National Institutes of Health that studies cancer.

Necrosis. Localized death of tissue.

Neoplasm. A new or abnormal tissue growth that is uncontrollable and progressive.

Nephrotoxic. Poisonous to the kidneys.

Neuritis. Inflammation of the nerves.

Neutralize. To render less chemically reactive; to change the pH to about 7 (neutral) by adding acid to a basic compound or base to an acidic compound.

NFPA. National Fire Protection Association. An international voluntary membership organization formed to promote/improve fire protection and prevention and establish safeguards against loss of life and property by fire. Best known for the National Fire Codes, 16 volumes of standards, recommended practices, and manuals developed (and periodically updated) by NFPA committees. NFPA 704M publication is the code for showing hazards of materials using the familiar diamond-shaped label with appropriate numbers or symbols (NFPA hazard rating). See Fire Diamond. (Batterymarch Park, Quincy, MA 02269; [800] 344-3555, [617] 770-3000)

NFPA Hazard Rating. See Fire Diamond.

ng. Nanogram. One billionth, 10^{-9}, of a gram.

NIOSH. National Institute of Occupational Safety and Health. The agency of the Public Health Service that tests and certifies respiratory and air-sampling devices. It recommends exposure limits to OSHA for substances, investigates incidents, and researches occupational safety. (NIOSH, 4676 Columbia Parkway, Cincinnati, OH 45226; [513] 533-8328.)

NLM. National Library of Medicine. A government library in Bethesda, Maryland containing medical documents.

NOC. Not otherwise classified.

NOEL. No observable effect level.

Nonflammable. Incapable of easy ignition. Does not burn, or burns very slowly. Also, a DOT hazard class for any compressed gas other than a flammable one.

NOR. Not otherwise regulated.

NOS. Not otherwise specified.

NO_x. A general formula for oxides of nitrogen (NO, NO_2). They react with moisture in the respiratory tract to produce acids that corrode and irritate tissue, causing congestion and pulmonary edema. Symptoms of acute exposure can develop over 6 to 24 hours. Chronic exposure to low levels can cause irritation, cough, headache, and tooth corrosion. Exposure to 5 to 50 ppm of NO_2 can cause slowly evolving pulmonary edema. Commonly produced by combustion processes, including motor vehicle engines.

NPCA. National Paint and Coatings Association. The trade association of manufacturers that developed the HMIS labeling system. (1500 Rhode Island Avenue, NW, Washington, DC 20005; [202] 462-6272.) See HMIS.

NRC. National Response Center. A notification center that must be called if a substantial RQ (Reportable Quantity) is released, or an oil or chemical spill or other environmental accident occurs. (1-800-424-8802)

NTP. National Toxicology Program. Federal activity overseen by the Department of Health and Human Services with resources from the National Institutes of Health, the Food and Drug Administration, and the Centers for Disease Control. Its goals are to develop tests useful for public health regulations of toxic chemicals, to develop toxicological profiles of materials, to foster testing of materials, and to communicate the results for use by others. (NTP Information Office, MD E1-02, Box 12233, Research Triangle Park, NC 27709.)

Nuisance Particulates. Dusts that do not produce significant organic disease or toxic effect from "reasonable" concentrations and exposures. Otherwise known as "Particulates not otherwise classified" (PNOC). The 1992-93 ACGIH TLV is 10 mg/m^3. The value is for total dust containing no asbestos and less than 1% crystalline silica.

Nystagmus. Rapid, rhythmic, involuntary horizontal movements of the eyes.

Occupational Exposure. See Action Level.

Occupational Safety and Health Act. See OSH Act.

Occupational Safety and Health Administration. See OSHA.

Odor Threshold. The lowest concentration detectable by odor; published values vary greatly, as does an individual's ability to detect chemical odors; air monitoring is a much more reliable way to detect chemical hazards for many substances.

OEL. Occupational Exposure Limit. See Exposure Limits.

Oliguria. Scanty or low volume of urine.

Opaque. Impervious to light rays.

Open Transfer. Any transfer that at any time involves contact of a moving fluid with atmosphere, air, or oxygen. Open transfer of flammable liquids, especially Class IA liquids, is dangerous due to the release of flammable vapors into the work area. Since there is a risk of fire or explosion if an ignition source is present, do these transfers only in a hood.

Oral. An exposure route "through the mouth."

Organic Materials. Compounds composed of carbon, hydrogen, and other elements with chain or ring structures. Almost all chemical constituents of living matter are of this type; but many compounds of this type are manufactured and do not occur naturally.

Organic Peroxide. A compound containing the bivalent - O - O - structure and that is a structural derivative of hydrogen peroxide (H_2O_2) where one or both hydrogen atoms are replaced by an organic radical. These compounds tend to be reactive and unstable.

ORM. Other regulated material. DOT hazard classification of a particular hazardous material to label it in transport. **ORM-D:** materials such as consumer commodities that present limited hazards during transportation due to their form, quantity, and packaging.

OSHA. The Occupational Safety and Health Administration. Part of the U.S. Department of Labor. The regulatory and enforcement agency for safety and health in most U.S. industrial sectors. (Documents are available from the OSHA Technical Data Center Docket Office, Rm N-3670, 200 Constitution Ave, NW, Washington, DC 20210; [202] 219-7500.)

OSH Act. The *Occupational Safety and Health Act* of 1970. Effective April 28, 1971. Public Law 91-596. Found at 29 CFR 1910, 1915, 1918, 1926. OSHA jurisdiction. The regulatory vehicle to ensure the safety and health of workers in firms larger than 10 employees. Its goal is to set standards of safety that prevent injury and illness among the workers. Regulating employee exposure and informing employees of the dangers of materials are key factors. This act established the

Hazard Communication Rule (29 CFR 1910.1200).

OSHA Flammable/Combustible Liquid Classification. (29 CFR 1910.106). Flammable/combustible liquid is a standard classification used to identify the risks of fire or explosion associated with a liquid. Flammable, or Class I, liquids (flash point below 38 °C [100 °F]) are divided into: Class IA - flash point below 22.8 °C (73 °F), boiling point below 38 °C (100 °F); Class IB - flash point below 22.8 °C (73 °F), boiling point at or above 38 °C (100 °F); and Class IC - flash point at or above 22.8 °C (73 °F), boiling point below 38 °C (100 °F). Combustible liquids (flash point at or above 38 °C [100 °F]) are divided into two classes: Class II, flash point at or above 38 °C (100 °F) and below 60 °C (140 °F), except any mixture having components with flash points of 93.3 °C (200 °F) or higher, the volume of which makes up 99% or more of the mixture's total volume; and Class III, flash point at or above 60 °C (140 °F). Class III liquids are divided into two subclasses: Class IIIA, flash point at or above 60 °C (140 °F) and below 93.3 °C (200 °F), except any mixture having components with flash points of 93.3 °C (200 °F) or higher, the volume of which makes up 99% or more of the mixture's total volume; and Class IIIB, flash point at or above 93.3 °C (200 °F).

Oxidation. A reaction in which a substance combines with oxygen or another oxidizer.

Oxide Pox. Dermatitis caused by contact with metal oxides under poor personal hygienic conditions.

Oxidizer. The DOT defines an oxidizer as a substance that yields oxygen readily to cause or enhance combustion (oxidation) of other materials. Many oxidizers, such as chlorate (ClO_3), permanganate (MnO_4), and nitrate (NO_3) compounds contain large amounts of oxygen (O). Others, such as chlorine, do not.

Oxidizing Agent. A chemical or substance that brings about an oxidation reaction. The agent may 1) provide the oxygen to the substance being oxidized (in which case the agent has to be oxygen or contain oxygen), or 2) receive electrons being transferred from the substance undergoing oxidation. (Chlorine is a good oxidizing agent for electron-transfer purposes, even though it contains no oxygen.) See Reducing Agent.

PAH. See Polycyclic Aromatic Hydrocarbons.

Palpitation. Irregular, rapid heartbeat.

Paresthesias. Altered sensations of the skin, often numbness and tingling, or "pins and needles" sensation.

Particulates. Solid or liquid particles suspended in air; aerosol.

Partition Coefficient. See Coefficient of Water/Oil Distribution.

PCB. Polychlorinated biphenyl. A family of compounds used as a heat-transfer medium. PCB's accumulate in tissue, are environmentally hazardous, and are believed to be harmful to human health. Their handling is regulated by law (40 CFR Part 761).

PEL. Permissible Exposure Limit. Established by OSHA. This may be expressed as a time-weighted average (TWA) limit, a short-term exposure limit (STEL), or as a ceiling exposure limit. A ceiling limit must never be exceeded instantaneously even if the TWA exposure limit is not violated. OSHA PELs have the force of law. Note that ACGIH TLVs and NIOSH RELs are recommended exposure limits that OSHA may or may not enact into law.

Pensky-Martens Closed Cup or Closed Tester. See PMCC.

Percent Volatile. Percent volatile by volume. The percentage of a liquid or solid (by volume) that evaporates at an ambient temperature of 20 °C (70 °F) unless another temperature is stated. For example, gasoline and paint thinner (mineral spirits) are 100% volatile. Their individual evaporation rates vary, but over a period of time each evaporates completely. This physical characteristic reflects the potential for releasing harmful vapor into the air.

Percutaneous. Through the skin.

Peripheral Nervous System (PNS). Nerves outside of the brain and spinal cord, including motor nerves to control the function of muscles, sensory nerves to carry sensations to the brain, and autonomic nerves to control a variety of organ functions.

Permissible Exposure Limit. See PEL.

Personal Hygiene. Precautionary measures taken to maintain good health when exposed to potentially harmful materials. This includes keeping hands and other body parts, clothing, and equipment free of a material's residue, and not eating, drinking, applying makeup, or using toilet facilities where a material is in use.

Personal Protective Equipment. See PPE.

pH. Hydrogen ion exponent; a measure of hydrogen ion concentration of a solution. A scale (0 to 14) representing an aqueous solution's acidity or alkalinity. Low pH values indicate acidity and high values, alkalinity. The scale's midpoint, 7, is neutral. Some substances in aqueous solution ionize to various extents giving different concentrations of H and OH ions. Strong acids have excess H ions and a pH of 1 to 3 (HCl, pH = 1). Strong bases have excess OH ions and a pH of 11 to 13 (NaOH, pH = 12).

Phlegm. Thick mucous from respiratory passage.

Photophobia. Intolerance to light.

Physical Hazard. A substance for which there is valid evidence that it is a combustible liquid, compressed gas, explosive, flammable, an organic peroxide, an oxidizer, pyrophoric, unstable (reactive), or water reactive. In the general safety sense, a hazard of physical origin, such as a fall, a heat burn, etc., and not a chemical or infective disease hazard.

Physical State. The condition of a material; i.e. solid, liquid, or gas, at room temperature.

PIN. Product identification number. A four-digit number, prefaced by UN or NA, used in Canada under the *Transportation of Dangerous Goods Regulation* for use by emergency personnel to identify a material in the event of an accident. See DOT Identification Numbers, the same numbering system used in the U.S.

PMCC. Pensky-Martens closed cup. One of several types of apparatus for determining flash points. The Pensky-Martens closed tester (ASTM D93-79) is used for liquids that: 1) have a viscosity of 45 SUS (Saybolt universal seconds) or more at 38 °C (100 °F); 2) have flash points of 93.6 °C (200 °F) or higher; 3) contain suspended solids; or 4) form surface films.

Pneumoconiosis. A respiratory tract and lung condition caused by inhalation and retention of irritant mineral or metallic particles. An X-ray can detect changes, including fibrosis and emphysema.

Pneumonia. Inflammatory lung disease caused by microorganisms, virus, and chemical or physical irritants.

PNOC. An ACGIH term for "particulates not otherwise classified". See Nuisance Particulates.

PNOR. An OSHA term for "particulates not otherwise regulated". (TWA: 15 mg/m^3, total dust; 5 mg/m^3, respirable fraction).

PNS. See Peripheral Nervous System.

Poison Control Center. Provides medical information on a 24-hour basis for accidents involving ingestion of potentially poisonous materials. Call your area's largest hospital to find the one nearest you.

Poisonous Material. A material, other than a gas, that is known (on the basis of animal tests) to be so toxic to humans or causes such extreme irritation as to afford a hazard to health.

Polycyclic Aromatic Hydrocarbons (PAH). A family of chemical compounds containing only carbon and hydrogen, in which molecules consist of three or more carbon ring structures fused so that some carbon atoms are common to two or three rings. A large number of this chemical family's members are carcinogens, or are converted to carcinogens when metabolized by animals or humans. PAHs are formed during incomplete combustion of hydrocarbons. They are common in smoke, such as that of vehicle exhaust or tobacco, and are also important industrial contaminants in coal gas or coke manufacture and other processes involving heating of coal tar and pitch.

Polymerization. A chemical reaction in which one or more small molecules combine to form larger molecules. Hazardous polymerization takes place at a rate that releases large amounts of energy that can cause fires or explosions or burst containers. Materials that can polymerize may usually contain inhibitors that can delay reactions.

Pour Point. The temperature at which a liquid either congeals or ceases to flow.

POx. A general term for the several oxides of phosphorus.

ppb. Parts per billion.

PPE. Personal protective equipment. Devices or clothing worn to help isolate a worker from direct exposure to hazardous materials. Examples include gloves, respirators, safety glasses, or ear plugs.

ppm. Parts per million. "Parts of vapor or gas per million parts of air by volume at 25 °C and 1 atm pressure" (ACGIH). At 25 °C, ppm = (mg/m^3 x 24.45) divided by molecular weight.

ppt. Parts per trillion.

Precordial. In front of the heart, stomach.

Product Identification Number. See PIN.

Prostration. A state of total mental or physical exhaustion.

Protective Laboratory Practices and Equipment. As defined by OSHA 1910.1450 Lab standard, those laboratory procedures, practices, and equipment that laboratory health and safety experts accept as effective, or that the employer can show are effective, in minimizing the potential for employee exposure to hazardous chemicals.

Proteinuria. Presence of protein in the urine.

psia. Pounds per square inch absolute.

psig. Pounds per square inch gauge (i.e. above atmospheric pressure).

Psychotropic, PSY. Acting on the mind.

Pulmonary Edema. Fluid in the lungs.

Purge. To clean, clear, or empty of material; a bleed of air or inert gas into a vessel to remove or exclude contaminants.

Pyrolysis. A chemical decomposition or breaking apart of molecules produced by heating.

Pyrophoric. Describes a material even in a small quantity that, without an external ignition source, can ignite within five minutes after coming in contact with air.

RCRA. *Resource Conservation and Recovery Act*, PL 94-580. Found at 40 CFR 240-271. EPA has jurisdiction. Enacted November 21, 1976, and amended since. RCRA's major emphasis is the control of hazardous waste disposal. It controls all solid-waste disposal and encourages recycling and alternative energy sources.

RCRA Hazardous Waste. A material designated by RCRA as a hazardous waste and assigned a number to be used in recordkeeping and reporting compliance (e.g. D003, F001, U169).

Reactive Flammable Material. A material that is a fire hazard because it reacts readily with air or water. Included are materials that: 1) spontaneously ignite in air or water; 2) react vigorously with air; and 3) give off flammable gas on reaction with water. Keep these materials dry and away from oxidizers. They are often stored in an all-nitrogen or argon environment.

Reactive Material. A chemical substance or mixture that vigorously polymerizes, decomposes, condenses, or becomes self-reactive due to shock, pressure, or temperature. Includes materials or mixtures within any of these categories: 1) **explosive material** - a substance or mixture that causes sudden, almost instantaneous release of pressure, gas, and heat when subjected to sudden adverse conditions; 2) **organic peroxide** - an organic compound that contains the bivalent -O-O- structure, which can be considered a structural derivative of hydrogen peroxide, in which one or both of the hydrogen atoms has been replaced by an organic radical; 3) **pressure-generating material** - a substance or mixture that spontaneously polymerizes with an increase in pressure unless protected by the addition of an inhibitor or by refrigeration or other thermal control, decomposes to release gas in its container, or comprises the contents of a self-pressurized container; and 4) **water-reactive material** - a substance or mixture that reacts with water releasing heat or flammable, toxic gas.

Reactivity. A substance's tendency to undergo chemical reaction either by itself or with other materials with the release of energy. Undesirable effects such as pressure buildup, temperature increase, or formation of noxious, toxic, or corrosive by-products may occur because of the substance's reactivity to heating, burning, direct contact with other materials, or other conditions in use or in storage. A solid waste that exhibits a "characteristic of reactivity", as defined by RCRA, may be regulated (by the EPA) as a hazardous waste and assigned the number D003.

Reagent. Substance used in a chemical reaction to aid in qualitative or quantitative analysis of another substance.

Recommended Exposure Limit. See REL.

Reducing Agent. In a reduction reaction (that always occurs simultaneously with an oxidation reaction), the reducing agent is the chemical or substance that: 1) combines with oxygen; or 2) loses electrons to the reaction. See Oxidation; Oxidizing Agent.

REL. The NIOSH REL (Recommended Exposure Limit) is the highest allowable airborne concentration that is not expected to injure a worker. It may be expressed as a ceiling limit or as a time-weighted average (TWA), usually for 10-hour work shifts.

Reportable Quantity. See RQ.

Reproductive Health Hazard/Toxin. Any agent with a harmful effect on the adult male or female reproductive systems or on the developing fetus or child. Such hazards affect people in many ways, including loss of sexual drive, mental disorders, impotence, infertility, sterility, mutagenic effects on germ cells, teratogenic effects on the fetus, and transplacental carcinogenesis.

Resource Conservation and Recovery Act. See RCRA.

Respirator. A variety of devices that limit inhalation of toxic materials. They range from disposable dust masks to self-contained breathing apparatus (SCBA). All have specific uses and limitations. Their use is covered by OSHA, 29 CFR 1910.134. See SCBA; Chemical Cartridge Respirator.

Respiratory System. The breathing system, including the lungs and air passage (trachea or windpipe, larynx, mouth, and nose).

Route of Entry or **Route of Exposure.** The way a chemical enters the body; inhalation, eye contact, skin contact/absorption, and ingestion.

RQ. Reportable Quantity. The amount of a material that, when spilled, must be reported to the DOT (Section 311 of the *Clean Water Act*).

RTECS. *Registry of Toxic Effects of Chemical Substances*, published by NIOSH. Presents basic toxicity data on thousands of materials. Its objective is to identify all known toxic substances and to reference the original studies.

SADT, Self-Accelerating Decomposition Temperature. A test that determines an organic peroxide's minimum unsafe storage temperature. This test describes an organic peroxide's tendency to decompose as it warms. Since organic peroxides are oxygen-containing organic compounds, they are both a fuel and an oxidizer. Decomposition can be violent. A related term is MSST, the Maximum Safe Storage Temperature.

Saint Andrew's Cross. X. Used in packaging for transport; means harmful; stow away from foodstuffs. (IMO, Material Class 6.1, Group III).

SARA. *Superfund Amendments and Reauthorization Act.* Signed into law October 17, 1986. Title III of SARA is known as the *Emergency Planning and Community Right-to-Know Act* of 1986. A revision and extension of CERCLA, SARA is intended to encourage and support local and state emergency planning efforts. It provides citizens and local governments with information about potential chemical hazards in their communities. SARA calls for facilities that store hazardous materials to provide officials and citizens with data on the types (flammables, corrosives, etc.); amounts on hand (daily, yearly); and specific locations. Facilities are to prepare and submit inventory lists, MSDSs, and tier 1 and 2 inventory forms. The 1987 disaster in Bhopal, India, added impetus to this law's passage.

SCBA. See Self-contained Breathing Apparatus.

SCC. See SETA; SETAFLASH Closed Tester.

Sclera. The tough, white, fibrous covering of the eyeball.

Select Carcinogen. See Carcinogen.

Self-Accelerating Decomposition Temperature. See SADT.

Self-contained Breathing Apparatus (SCBA). A respirator which contains its own air supply that the user carries, usually in a tank on his or her back (very similar to scuba gear).

Sensitization. A state of immune-response reaction in which exposure to a material elicits an immune or allergic response.

Sensitizer. A material that on first exposure causes little or no reaction in humans or test animals, but upon repeated exposure may cause a marked response not necessarily limited to the contact site. Skin sensitization is the most common form. Respiratory sensitization to a few chemicals also occurs.

SETA, SETAFLASH Closed Tester. Apparatus used to measure flash points in liquids in the 0 °C to 110 °C (32 °F to 230 °F) range (ASTM D 3278-82).

Siderosis. Pneumoconiosis caused by inhalation of iron particles. Also, tissue pigmentation caused by contact with iron.

Silicosis. A condition of massive fibrosis of the lungs causing shortness of breath because of prolonged inhalation of silica dusts.

Skin. A notation to exposure limits (TLVs) indicating possible significant contribution to overall exposure to a material by way of absorption through the skin, mucous membranes, and eyes by direct or airborne contact.

Slurry. A pourable mixture of solid and liquid.

Smoke. Dry particles and droplets (usually carbon or soot) generated by incomplete combustion of an organic material combined with and suspended in the gases from combustion.

Solubility in Water. A term expressing the percentage of a material (by weight) that dissolves in water at ambient temperature. Solubility information is useful in determining cleanup methods for spills and fire-extinguishing methods for a material. Solubility may be expressed as negligible, less than 0.1%; slight, 0.1 to 1.0%; moderate, 1 to 10%; appreciable, more than 10%; complete, soluble in all proportions. Alternatively, and more usually, it may be expressed as a percentage by weight in a solution, as grams of solute per liter of solution, or as grams of solute dissolved in 100 g of water.

Solution, Soln. A uniformly dispersed single-phase mixture of a solvent (water or other fluid) and a dissolved substance, called the solute.

Solvent. A material that can dissolve other materials to form a uniform single-phase mixture. Water is the most common solvent.

Soot. Fine particles, usually black, formed by combustion (complete or incomplete) and consisting chiefly of carbon. Soot gives smoke its color.

SO_x. Oxides of sulfur where x equals the number of oxygen atoms.

Spasm. An involuntary, convulsive muscular contraction.

SPCC. Spill Prevention, Control, and Counter-measure plan.

Specific Gravity. The ratio of the density of a substance to the density of a reference substance, at a specified temperature. Specific gravity is a dimensionless number. Water (density 1 kg/l or 1 g/mL or 1 g/cm^3 at 4 °C) is the reference for solids and liquids, while air (density 1.29 g/l at 0 °C and 760 mm Hg pressure) is the reference for gases. If a volume of a material weighs 8 g, and an equal volume of water weighs 10 g, the material has a specific gravity of 0.8 ($8 \div 10 = 0.8$). Insoluble materials with specific gravity greater than 1.0 will sink (or go to the bottom) in water. Specific gravity is an important fire suppression and spill cleanup consideration since most (but not all) flammable liquids have a specific gravity less than 1.0 and, if insoluble, float on water.

Spontaneously Combustible Material. A material which undergoes self-heating to the point of ignition without requiring heat from another source.

Stability. The ability of a material to remain unchanged. For MSDS purposes, a material is stable if it remains in the same form under expected and reasonable conditions of storage or use. Conditions such as temperatures above 66 °C (150 °F) or shock from being dropped that may cause instability (dangerous change) are stated on the MSDS. See Unstable.

STEL. Short-term exposure limit; ACGIH terminology. See TLV-STEL.

Stomatitis. Inflammation of the mucous membrane of the mouth.

Stupor. Partial or near complete unconsciousness.

Subcutaneous. Beneath the skin.

Sublime. To change from the solid to the vapor phase without passing through the liquid phase. Dry ice exhibits sublimation.

Subpart Z. See Z List.

Superfund Amendments and Reauthorization Act. See SARA; CERCLA.

SUS. Saybolt Universal Seconds. A unit measure of viscosity determined by the number of seconds required for an oil heated to 54 °C (130 °F) (lighter oils) and 99 °C (210 °F) (heavier oils) to flow through a standard orifice and fill a 60-ml flask.

Synergism. A combined action of two or more toxic substances to give an effect greater than the sum of their activity when each toxic substance is alone. For example, both smoking and exposure to asbestos can cause lung cancer; however, if a smoker is also exposed to asbestos, the danger of lung cancer is far greater than just adding together the separate risks from the two exposures.

Synonyms. Alternative names by which a material may be known.

Tachycardia. Excessively rapid heartbeat, usually with a pulse rate above 100 beats per minute.

Tachypnea. Increased rate of respiration.

Tag Closed Cup. See TCC or TCT.

Tag Open Cup. See TOC.

Tag Open Tester. An open-tank tester for liquids with low flash points. See TCC or TCT.

Target Organ Effects. Chemically-caused effects from exposure to a material on specific listed organs and systems such as the liver, kidneys, nervous system, lungs, skin, and eyes.

TCC or TCT. Tag (Tagliabue) closed cup or Tag closed tester. One of several types of apparatus for determining flash points. The Tag closed tester, per ASTM D56-79, is intended for testing liquids with a viscosity of less than 45 SUS at 38 °C (100 °F) and a flash point below 93.4 °C (200 °F). Liquids should not have suspended solids or form surface films.

TC_{Lo}. Toxic concentration low. The lowest concentration of a substance in air to which humans or animals have been exposed for any given period of time that has produced any toxic effect in humans or produced a tumorigenic or reproductive effect in animals or humans.

TD_{Lo}. The lowest dose of a substance introduced by any route other than inhalation over any given period of time and reported to produce any toxic effect in humans or to produce tumorigenic or reproductive effects in animals or humans.

Temp. Temperature.

Teratogen. Agent or material causing physical defects in a developing embryo.

Threshold Limit Value. See TLV.

Threshold Planning Quantity (TPQ). Per 40 CFR 302. The amount of material at a facility that requires emergency planning and notification per CERCLA.

Time-Weighted Average. See TLV.

Tinnitus. A ringing sound in the ears.

TLm. Median tolerance limit. Designates a toxic material's concentration at which 50% of the test organisms, usually aquatic, survive. For example, a conservation authority may limit pollution to TL_{90} (at which 90% survival is required), to protect fish.

TLV. Threshold limit value. A term ACGIH uses to express the maximum airborne concentration of a material to which *most* workers can be exposed during a normal daily and weekly work schedule without adverse effects. "Workers" means healthy individuals; "healthy" is defined as a 150 lb. male, age 25 to 44. The young, old, ill, or naturally susceptible have lower tolerances and need to take additional precautions. ACGIH expresses TLVs in three ways: 1) **TLV-TWA**, the allowable time-weighted average concentration for a normal 8-hour workday or 40-hour week; 2) **TLV-STEL**, the short-term exposure limit or maximum concentration for a continuous exposure period of 15 minutes (with a maximum of four such periods per day, with at least 60 minutes between exposure periods, and provided that the daily TLV-TWA is not exceeded); and 3) **Ceiling** (C), the concentration not to exceed at any time.

TLV-Ceiling Limit. TLV-C. The ceiling exposure limit or concentration not to exceed at any time, even for very brief times. The ACGIH publishes a book annually that explains and lists TLVs called *Threshold Limit Values for Chemical Substances and Physical Agents and Biological Exposure Indices*. Copies are available from ACGIH (q.v.).

TLV-Skin. See Skin.

TOC. Tag open-cup test method.

torr. A unit of pressure, equal to 1 mm Hg. See atm (atmosphere).

Toxic. Poisonous; having properties of causing adverse health effects when the body is exposed. Having 1) an LD_{50} of 50 to 500 mg/kg when administered orally to albino rats weighing 200 to 300 g each; 2) an LD_{50} of 200 to 1000 mg/kg when administered by continuous contact for 24 hours to the bare skin of albino rabbits weighing 2 to 3 kg each; or 3) an LC_{50} of 200 to 2000 ppm (gas or vapor) or 2 to 20 mg/l (mist, fume, or dust) when administered by continuous inhalation for 1 hour to albino rats weighing 200 to 300 g each. See Acute Toxicity.

Toxicology. The study of the nature, effects, and detection of poisons in living organisms. Also, substances that are otherwise harmless but prove toxic under certain conditions. The basic assumption of toxicology is that there is a relationship among the dose (amount), the concentration at the affected site, and the resulting effects.

Toxic Substance. Any chemical or material that: 1) has evidence of an acute or chronic health hazard and 2) is listed in the NIOSH *Registry of Toxic Effects of Chemical Substances* (RTECS), provided that the substance causes harm at any dose level; causes cancer or reproductive effects in animals at any dose level; has a median lethal dose (LD_{50}) of less than 500 mg/kg of body weight when administered orally to rats; has a median LD_{50} of less than 1000 mg/kg of body weight when administered by continuous contact to the bare skin of albino rabbits; or has a median lethal concentration (LC_{50}) in air of less than 2000 ppm by volume of gas or vapor, or less than 20 mg/L of mist, fume, or dust when administered to albino rats.

Toxic Substances Control Act. See TSCA.

TPQ. See Threshold Planning Quantity.

Tradename. A name, usually not the chemical name, given to a product by the manufacturer or supplier and usually protected as a Registered Trademark. The same or similar products can be marketed under different tradenames by different companies.

Trade Secret. Confidential information (formula, process, device, etc.) that gives the owner an advantage over competitors. Manufacturers may choose to withhold proprietary data from an MSDS. Typically these would be ingredients of a formulated product. OSHA permits this provided that: 1) the trade secret claim can be substantiated; 2) the MSDS indicates that data is being withheld; and 3) the properties and health effects are included. State laws vary on this practice; some states require a trade secret registration number to be assigned to a material. There are procedures to obtain necessary trade secret information in emergency situations.

TSCA. *Toxic Substances Control Act.* Public Law PL 94-469. Found in 40 CFR 700-799. EPA has jurisdiction. Effective Jan. 1, 1977. Controls the exposure to and use of raw industrial chemicals not subject to other laws. Chemicals are to be evaluated prior to use and can be controlled based on risk. The act provides for a listing of all chemicals that are to be evaluated prior to manufacture or use in the U.S. (EPA, Industry Assistance Office, [202] 554-1404.)

Tumor. A growth of tissue without physiological function. May be benign (noninvasive) or cancerous. See Cancer; Neoplasm.

TWA. Time-weighted average. See TLV-TWA.

UEL. See Upper Explosive Limit; Upper Flammable Limit.

UFL. See Upper Flammable Limit; Upper Explosive Limit.

Ulcer. Loss or death of tissue resulting in an open sore on the skin or on a surface of an internal organ, such as the stomach.

UN Number. See DOT Identification Numbers; PIN.

Unstable. Tending toward decomposition or other unwanted chemical change during normal handling or storage. An unstable chemical in its pure state, or as commonly produced or transported, polymerizes vigorously, decomposes, condenses, or becomes self-reactive under conditions of shock, pressure, or temperature. See Stability; Reactive Material.

Upper Explosive Limit, Upper Flammable Limit. UEL, UFL. The highest concentration of a material in air that produces an explosion or fire, or that ignites when it contacts an ignition source (high heat, electric arc, spark, or flame). Any concentration above the UEL in air is too rich to be ignited. See Flammable Limits.

Urticaria. Hives caused by a systemic allergic reaction.

UV. Ultraviolet (light).

Vapor. The gaseous state of a material normally encountered as liquid or solid.

Vapor Density. The ratio of the formula mass (FM) of the compound to the average formula mass of the gases in air (29 grams per mole). This formula mass ratio is correct for a pure gas at room temperature. However, this ratio does not accurately express the vapor density of a liquid solvent. A liquid cannot liberate vapors more concentrated than its saturated vapor concentration. The saturated vapor concentration of a liquid is the ratio of its vapor pressure at a given temperature to the atmospheric pressure. Using this ratio, the % of the compound in air and the remaining % of air at saturation (for example, 19.7% hexane and 80.3% air) can be calculated. The saturated vapor density is then determined by multiplying the % of the compound in air by its FM and the % of air by its FM; adding this air/liquid vapor mixture at saturation; and dividing the sum by 29 and multiplying by the density of pure air (1.2 kg/m^3, 0.075 lbs/ft^3). Saturated air/liquid vapor mixtures may be heavier than air, but not as heavy as formula mass ratios indicate. Temperature differences and turbulence create density differences between volumes of air and often have a greater influence on the movement of contaminated air than the actual saturated vapor density of the chemical.

Vapor Pressure. The pressure a saturated vapor exerts above its own liquid in a closed container. Vapor pressures reported on MSDSs are usually stated in millimeters of mercury (mm Hg) at 20 °C (68 °F). The lower a substance's boiling point, the higher its vapor pressure; and the higher the vapor pressure, the greater the material's tendency to evaporate into the atmosphere. Vapor pressures are useful (with evaporation rates) in learning how quickly a material becomes airborne within the workplace and thus how quickly a worker is exposed to it.

Vertigo. A feeling of revolving in space; dizziness, giddiness.

Viscosity. Measurement of a fluid's thickness or resistance to flow. Unit of measurement, usually centipoise (cP), and temperature are included.

VOC. Volatile organic compounds. Used in coatings and paint because they evaporate very rapidly. Regulated by the EPA per the *Clean Water Act*.

Volatility. Measure of a material's tendency to vaporize or evaporate at ambient routine conditions.

VP. See Vapor Pressure.

Water Reactive. A material that by contact with water becomes spontaneously flammable or gives off a flammable or toxic gas and presents a health hazard.

Working Alone. Performance of any work by an individual out of audio or visual range of another individual for more than a few minutes. No other person is aware of the individual working alone, the nature of the work being done, or the time period the individual expects to work. A worker alone in a lab should not undertake experiments known to be hazardous. Always work under conditions where the availability of emergency aid is compatible with the nature of the hazard and the degree of exposure.

Zinc Fume Fever. Caused by inhalation of zinc oxide fume and characterized by flu-like symptoms: metallic taste in mouth, coughing, weakness, fatigue, muscular pain, and nausea, followed by fever and chills. Symptoms occur 4 to 12 hours after exposure.

Z List. OSHA's Toxic and Hazardous Substances Tables Z-1-A, Z-2, and Z-3 of air contaminants, (29 CFR 1910.1000). These tables record TWAs, STELs, and ceiling concentrations for the materials listed. Any material on these tables is considered hazardous.

NOTES

NOTES

NOTES

NOTES

Have you been paying attention? Prove it!

1. What is the name of the law that protects laboratory employees?

____

____

____

2. Different types of gloves protect against different classes of chemicals.

True False

3. What was the final diagnosis of Cheryl's condition?

____

4. Briefly, what caused Cheryl's condition?

____

____

____

5. How could Cheryl have avoided this condition?

____

____

____

Name: ______________________ **Course:** ____________

Instructor: ____________________ **Date:** ____________

Have you been paying attention? Prove it!

1. Name two criteria used to determine if a chemical is hazardous.

____

____

2. What is the most likely route of entry for exposure to chemicals?

____

3. What can happen when certain chemicals, like the one that injured Cheryl, absorb through your skin?

____

____

____

____

4. What is the difference between acute and chronic exposure?

____

____

____

____

Name: ______________________ **Course:** ____________

Instructor: ______________________ **Date:** ____________

Have you been paying attention? Prove it!

1. Define and explain the following terms:

   TWA ____

   ____

   ____

   TLV-STEL ____

   ____

   ____

   Ceiling ____

   ____

   ____

   IDLH ____

   ____

   ____

   PEL ____

   ____

   ____

2. Which governmental agency's exposure limits are enforced by law?

   ACGIH NIOSH OSHA

3. What is LD_{50}? ____

   ____

4. How is toxicity data obtained and how is it used? ____________________

   ____

   ____

Name: ______________________________ **Course:** ______________

Instructor: ____________________________ **Date:** ______________

Have you been paying attention? Prove it!

1. Name five common hazard warnings.

____

____

____

____

____

2. Why are hazard warnings important? _______________

____

____

3. What are the characteristics of a flammable material? _______________

____

____

Give two examples. _______________

____

4. What are the characteristics of an explosive material? _______________

____

____

Give two examples. _______________

____

Name: _______________ **Course:** _______________

Instructor: _______________ **Date:** _______________

Have you been paying attention? Prove it!

1. What is an MSDS and what is its purpose?____________________

2. Name four types of information that must be included on an MSDS.

3. What is synergy? Give an example. ____________________

4. Name three types of physical data given on an MSDS?

5. What is a flash point? ____________________

Name: ____________________ **Course:** __________

Instructor: ____________________ **Date:** __________

Have you been paying attention? Prove it!

1. What are three steps to follow in case of an incident involving a hazardous material? Why is each step important?

____

____

____

____

____

____

2. Why is it sometimes best to *not* induce vomiting after ingestion of a chemical, such as a corrosive or a solvent?

____

____

____

____

3. What are the dangers of pressure build-up in a flask of flammable boiling liquid?

____

____

____

____

Name: ______________________ **Course:** ____________

Instructor: ___________________ **Date:** ____________

Have you been paying attention? Prove it!

1. Name and briefly explain the ten steps to follow in case of a spill.

Name: ______________________ **Course:** ______________

Instructor: ______________________ **Date:** ______________

Have you been paying attention? Prove it!

1. What are the four basic types of personal protective equipment used in a chemistry lab?

____

____

____

____

2. This book's position on contact lenses is as follows: Contact lens use in the lab is acceptable and does not create an additional hazard for the wearer.

True False

3. What types of clothing should not be worn in the lab?

____

____

____

4. In what instances should you remove your gloves and exchange them for another pair?

____

____

____

5. What is a respirator designed to do?

____

____

____

Name: ______________________ **Course:** ____________

Instructor: ______________________ **Date:** ____________

Have you been paying attention? Prove it!

1. Name three precautions you should take when putting a glass tube through a hole in a rubber stopper.

____

____

____

2. Name two important precautions to take when working with each of the following pieces of laboratory equipment:

Lasers ___________________________________

____

____

Compressed Gases__________________________

____

____

Vacuum Desiccator _________________________

____

____

3. Name four precautions you should take to ensure that you operate a distillation system safely and properly.

____

____

____

____

Name: ______________________ **Course:** ______________

Instructor: ___________________ **Date:** ______________

Have you been paying attention? Prove it!

1. What is OSHA and what is its function?____________________

2. What does the *Hazard Communication* standard require employers to do?

3. What three pieces of information are required by OSHA to appear on a container label?

4. Briefly describe a *Chemical Hygiene Plan.* ____________________

5. Name two types of bloodborne pathogens.

Name: ____________________ **Course:** __________

Instructor: ____________________ **Date:** __________

Have you been paying attention? Prove it!

1. Why can't you dispose of all chemicals by dumping them in the drain?

____

____

____

2. Briefly describe the following:

Clean Air Act. ____

____

____

Clean Water Act. ____

____

____

Resource Conservation and Recovery Act. ____

____

____

Superfund Amendments and Reauthorization Act. ____

____

____

Comprehensive Environmental Response, Compensation, and Liability Act. ____

____

____

3. Name 3 of the characteristics used to classify a RCRA hazardous waste?

____

____

____

Name: ______________________ **Course:** ______________________

Instructor: ______________________ **Date:** ______________________